Country Living Answers

Draft Animals

100 Answers for Harnessing Animal Power

Michelle Lindsey

Country Living Answers

Draft Animals

100 Answers for Harnessing Animal Power

Michelle Lindsey

Homestead on the

— RANGE —

Abundant Living in Flyover Country

Published by Homestead on the Range
Derby, Kansas
https://homesteadontherange.com/

Homestead on the Range is a Kansas-based small business dedicated to serving country living enthusiasts by supplying them with the innovative resources that they need to succeed. Whether your family's farm or ranch is 5 acres or 500, a business or a hobby, in Kansas or in some other part of the world, our goal is to keep you informed and inspired.

Disclaimer

This publication contains materials designed to assist readers and for educational purposes. While the author and publisher have made every attempt to verify that the information provided in this book is correct and up to date, neither the author nor the publisher assumes any responsibility for any error, inaccuracy, or omission.

ISBN 978-0-9975261-5-8 (paperback)
ISBN 978-0-9975261-6-5 (eBook)

Contents

Introduction

Have you been longing to experience the nostalgia of working with a quiet draft horse team on a crisp, cool morning? Introduce oxen to your woodlot to harvest trees without damaging the land? Share the joy of draft animals with visitors to your farm?

For many homesteaders and small farmers with a focus on sustainability, draft animals are a natural consideration. There's just one problem—good information on getting started with draft animals is hard to come by in our mechanized age.

The good old days when your family passed down its draft animal know-how for generations are gone for most people. In many places, finding a neighbor with this expertise is not an option, either.

While we all recognize that hands-on learning with an experienced mentor is ideal, when it comes to draft animals, sometimes there is little choice but to hit the books. Unfortunately, books on draft animals are scarce, too. Books for the beginner covering preliminary decisions and all the draft animal species are even scarcer.

What's a beginner to do?

About This Book

Draft Animals seeks to fill the gap by covering common questions beginners ask in these 10 major areas:

- Whether or not draft animals are right for you.
- Choosing a species.
- Choosing a breed.
- Buying your first draft animals.
- Care and feeding.
- Equipment (yokes, harnesses, carts, implements, etc.).
- Working with draft animals.
- Training tips.
- Raising your own draft animals.
- The fun stuff you always wanted to know.

This book focuses on oxen, horses, mules, and donkeys, but also covers less traditional draft animals, such as goats, llamas, and dogs.

You will notice that this book uses a unique Q&A format. This approach is intended to cut straight to the chase and focus on the things beginners need to know purchase and start working with draft animals.

These questions were pulled from a variety of sources to give a good sample of the challenges newbies face as they seek draft animals and learn how to work with them in an era dominated by technologically advanced machinery. Some are questions that bring readers to websites like Homestead on the Range regularly. Others are typed into forums and search engines on a recurring basis.

Draft Animals is therefore by no means a complete guide. It was designed to deliver concise answers to beginners' most pressing questions, providing them with the tools they need to acquire some firsthand experience.

Tips for Using This Book

1. Browse through the pages to get a handle on the commitment required to keep a draft team.

2. Once you have a rough idea of what is involved, read the book more thoroughly. Take time to weigh the pros and cons of draft animals and determine if they are truly right for you.

3. Choose a species and a breed.

4. Once you have made these important decisions, you will be ready to buy one or more draft animals. Take a look at the questions on making the purchase, and also consult the "Helpful Resources" section toward the back of the book. You will find information in both places that will help you choose a reputable source to purchase your animals from. If you make this selection wisely, you will have found a valuable advisor—even if this person does not have experience using animals for draft purposes, he or she will definitely know a great deal about the breed and its care.

5. After consulting your new mentor and reading the advice contained in the chapter on care and feeding, prepare your farm for your new draft animals and bring them home.

6. Next turn your attention to acquiring the right equipment for your draft team and to learning how to work with animals. Again, two chapters and the resources in the back will help you get started.

7. You will encounter challenges along the way, and you may find your ambition growing as you become accustomed to working with draft animals. You may become curious about training or retraining a draft animal, or perhaps about breeding and raising your own draft animals. While you will want more information before you tackle either project, this book will hopefully point you in the right direction.

The last chapter will present interesting facts about draft animal history and biology. It is mostly for fun, although you will pick up some insights along the way.

Please keep in mind that *Draft Animals* is just a starting point. It cannot replace the lifetime of insight a good mentor can provide, nor can it substitute for the hands-on experience you will need. However, it should be able to answer some of your most important questions about getting started, and it should also guide you to more advanced information (see the "Helpful Resources" section in the back).

Chapter 1
Are Draft Animals Right for You?

There are many reasons you might be considering draft animals. Perhaps you are seeking to farm in a way that is more ecologically friendly. Perhaps draft animals are just the right addition to your agritourism enterprise. Or maybe you simply love horses.

Draft animals still have a place in modern agriculture. The key is to be aware of their strengths and weaknesses so that you can fit them into the right niche.

An Introduction to Draft Animals

1. What is a draft animal?

A draft animal is any animal used to aid in heavy labor by pulling a load. Draft animals are usually used either for agriculture or for transportation.

The traditional draft animals in the United States are oxen, horses, and mules, although donkeys are also common. More unusual draft animals include goats, sheep, llamas, alpacas, and dogs.

2. What are draft animals used for?

Modern uses for draft animals include:

- Forestry and logging.
- Market gardening.
- Cash-cropping.
- Haying.
- Transportation of people and goods.
- Power generation.
- Parades and publicity.
- Recreational driving.
- Various forms of competition.

Draft animals can perform numerous tasks within each major area. For instance, a team used for agricultural purposes may participate in roles as varied as plowing, cultivating, spreading soil amendments, and hauling a wagon to transport the harvest at the end of the season. Likewise, a team that normally pulls hay can just as easily haul farm guests. Your imagination is really the only limit in determining what a draft team can do.

Draft Animals in the Modern World

3. Why are draft animals important?

This is a very natural question to ask in today's mechanized world. After all, tractors replaced draft animals in America due to their greater efficiency in commodity farming. So who would use draft animals now?

As it turns out, draft animals have several advantages over machinery:

- **Nostalgia.** For some, that's reason enough!
- **Relaxed pace.** If you have a small acreage and are farming because you love it, why rush? The slower pace of draft animals gives you a good excuse to go outside and enjoy nature.
- **Less initial cost.** Depending on the type of animal you buy and where you buy it, you can probably pick up a good draft team and its equipment for less money than you could a good tractor. (You may be able to save money even further by making your own yokes, carts, and the like.)
- **Fuel savings.** Diesel and gasoline are not always cheap!
- **Maneuverability on difficult terrain.** Draft animals can work on slopes and in dense woodlots where no tractor, truck, or other machine can go. They are pretty good at off-roading, even in wet conditions.
- **Low impact on the land.** Draft animals do not compact the soil as badly as machinery does. In forestry applications, they are less likely to inadvertently hit and damage young trees, and they also permit the woodlot owner to selectively harvest trees rather than clear-cut (the practice of harvesting a whole swath of forest).
- **Fertilizer.** Unlike a tractor, a draft animal can make a huge contribution to the farm's soil fertility.
- **Self-sustainability.** If you decide to breed draft horses, you can easily raise replacements for your team. Plus, selling the surplus foals can help you cover your expenses.
- **A use for surplus bull calves.** Do you keep a dairy cow? Castrate her bull calf and put him to work!
- **Versatility.** When not in use for draft purposes, draft animals can often serve other roles on the farm. Draft horses can be ridden, donkeys can guard other livestock, and goats can devour brush and weeds.

- **Agritourism opportunities.** If you are interested in agritourism, you can find a wide variety of work for your draft team from hay rides to plowing demonstrations.

In short, there are several reasons why you might use draft animals on your farm instead of a tractor:

- For the love of it.
- To reduce startup costs in small operations.
- To reduce the negative impact of agriculture and forestry on the land.
- To complement other farm enterprises.
- To enhance public relations and draw new visitors to your farm.
- To create a self-sustaining closed-loop system.

All these considerations and applications make draft animals still well worth considering today, even in developed countries.

4. Are people who use draft animals a dying breed?

The future is currently looking brighter for draft animals than it has in a good many years. As younger generations display an interest in sustainable agriculture, whether for home food production or for small business purposes, draft animals have received renewed attention.

One of the biggest problems currently facing a potential new generation of animal-powered farmers is a daunting knowledge gap. Except in Amish communities, relatively few older farmers know how to work with draft animals these days, which means there are very few mentors out there. Learning the ropes with draft animals takes a great deal of time, and time is a huge investment, especially for those who are trying to start a farm business and support a young family at the same time.

Nevertheless, some old-timers have been encouraged by the number of younger farmers willing to tackle the challenges of using draft animals. This trend has doubtless been encouraged by an interest in sustainability and minimalism.

Draft Animal Economics

5. What expenses are involved?

Of course, the expenses will vary by species, but be prepared to budget for the following when first starting out:

- The initial purchase cost of the team.
- Harness.
- Carts, implements, etc.
- Fencing supplies.
- A water system.
- Feeders for grain, hay, and mineral.
- Building materials for a field shelter.
- Grooming supplies.

After that, you will need to pay for recurring maintenance items:

- Hay.
- Feed.
- Salt.
- Mineral supplements.
- Hoof care.
- Veterinary care.
- Leather conditioner for harness.
- The cost of your time and labor.

There are ways to reduce many of these costs. To start with, you can save a great deal of money on a team if you are careful about what you purchase. If you have a milk cow already, you can save money by raising and training a steer calf as an ox rather than buying one. For horses, look for a sound but plain-looking animal—flashy draft horses can be quite expensive, but may be less serviceable. Donkeys are sometimes given away for free in some areas. Starting with a trained mule team is typically the most expensive option due to the time and effort required to train them well.

Equipment does not have to be cost-prohibitive. Farm auctions are one way to pick up discarded implements for inexpensive prices. You may also be able to save some money by building your own simple carts.

There are also ways to reduce feed costs, such as relying on forage or keeping a donkey instead of a horse. However, hard-working animals have higher energy requirements than pasture potatoes. And unlike a tractor, a horse, mule, or ox must be fed (even if that is just pasture and mineral) even when not in use.

Hoof and veterinary care will depend largely on species. Horses require the most care to work, while mules, donkeys, and oxen are less prone to breakdowns. Most draft animals do not require shoes unless working on rough or slick surfaces, but horses are somewhat more likely to need shoeing to correct a hoof defect.

On the subject of labor costs, if you already raise animals, a few more won't increase your chore time significantly. Replacing a tractor with a draft team on a small grain farm will increase the workload, however. Training your own draft animals will take time, as well.

6. Which are more economical, draft animals or tractors?

In some cases, the tractor will win and in others the horses will win, as there are many variables. A new compact tractor can cost anywhere between $12,000 and $22,000, depending on the horsepower. A flashy matched pair of trained Percheron geldings can cost up to $15,000.

But again, there are many variables. You could easily save thousands of dollars on a draft team by choosing horses that aren't so spectacular in appearance as our hypothetical matched Percherons; a decent trained horse may cost no more than $2,000 if he is nothing special to look at. You could also make money by buying mares instead of geldings and selling their foals for additional income.

Equipment cost is another variable. Buying new equipment for either a tractor or a draft team can be somewhat expensive. Buying used equipment for either can be quite affordable. With draft teams, you may even be able to build some things yourself, like ox yokes or simple carts, making the startup cost even less.

A major factor to take into consideration is the price of feed versus the price of diesel. These two figures change considerably over time, so you would be best served to do this math yourself. Keep in mind that the draft animal may continue to need feed, hay, or mineral even when not working, albeit in smaller quantities. (This is less of a problem with donkeys.)

But you must also factor in your needs. If you are haying on a small scale, a two-horsepower team may be sufficient for your purpose. However, if you need a front end loader, you would be better served to buy a tractor.

Looking at it from a broader perspective, the FAO estimated there were 271 agricultural tractors for every 100 square kilometers in the United States in 2007. Since the total land area of the U.S. is over 9.8

million square kilometers, this comes out to about 26,558,000 tractors across the country. The horsepower of agricultural tractors varies widely (somewhere between 85 and 450 horsepower or even higher). Given a median horsepower around 265, our nation's tractors output a power equivalent to over 7 billion horses.

Clearly, we have a lot of machine power in the field. Ironically, these 26 million tractors work about 237 million acres of crops (the total crop acreage in the U.S. reported to the FSA in 2019). One horse can plow one acre a day on average, which means 7 billion horses could plow 7 billion acres of cropland—in a single day! Whatever potential advantages our nation's tractors might have, these statistics would suggest that we are not using them in a particularly efficient way.

So how did machines ever gain the ascendency over draft animals in the first place? The answer is human labor costs. Working with horses adds an estimated 20% labor time to every task, assuming the farmer is experienced. Learning as you go adds even more time, as does using horses that are not trained or worked on a regular basis. How well this aspect turns out for you depends on how much your time costs and how many acres you have to work.

7. Can you really make money logging with horses?

Yes! People do it on a regular basis.

The key to making a good income logging with horses is to develop your expertise in felling and extracting timber. For one thing, greater experience will enable you to work faster, thus selling more logs in a given amount of time. For another thing, as your expertise grows, your services will become increasingly valuable to landowners who want to manage their woodlots sustainably.

One way to enhance your logging income is to develop several income streams. For a horse-based logging business, these streams could include the following:

- Selling sawlogs from your own woodlot.
- Selling firewood to homeowners.
- Providing custom logging services to small woodlot owners.
- Selling draft horse foals. (Hint: Increase the value of your draft foals by training them first.)
- Teaching workshops to beginners interested in logging.

A final requirement for making a good income from logging is to keep the value of your logs high. Because of the time and labor involved, harvesting low-value wood with draft animals is rarely economical. Growing high-value timber requires an up-front investment in the woodlot, as low-value trees must be cut or girdled so that more desirable trees can take their place. But over time the woodlot quality will improve, making frequent light harvests profitable. (This is in stark contrast to the way mechanized logging is done, where low-value timber is harvested in massive quantities.)

Chapter 2
Choosing a Species

E very species of draft animal has its own pros and cons that you should weigh before making your final decision. Start by taking a rough inventory of your needs:

- How much pulling power do you need?
- What type of animal will you be most comfortable working with?
- What is available at a price you can afford?

If you have a slightly larger farm with a steady supply of heavy work, you may want to consider working with oxen, horses, or mules. For smaller operations, it may be more economical to consider a donkey or perhaps something more unconventional, like a goat or a dog.

Draft Animals Compared

8. What is the best draft animal?

The answer to this question largely depends on the work you intend to do, how you intend to do it, and under what conditions. Each species has its own advantages and disadvantages that make it ideally suited to some production systems and poorly suited to others.

Oxen

The advantages of oxen include:

- **Dependable temperament.** In general (because individual animals vary widely), oxen are less flighty than horses and less willful than mules. Good oxen are calm, docile, and very trainable.
- **Stamina.** Oxen are known for their ability to work all day. A draft horse of a similar size can often pull far more weight than an ox in a short burst, but the ox can outlast the horse when performing normal farm work on a daily basis.
- **Low feed requirements.** While oxen may face stiff competition from donkeys in this regard, they definitely require less feed to work well than horses when working. They are far more forgiving when it comes to pasture quality, as well.
- **Robust health.** Oxen are far less prone to some of the ailments that can force a draft team to take sick leave. When genetically sound and properly cared for, oxen are much less likely to go lame than horses. Also, they are not prone to colic.
- **Simple harnessing systems.** Oxen typically require relatively simple yokes, rather than the elaborate harnesses used on horses. This is due to the structural differences between the two animals—an ox's strength is in his head and neck, while a horse is stronger through the chest. A well-made neck yoke is quite comfortable for an ox, but it would tend to choke a horse. This translates to less expense, less confusion, less maintenance, and less time spent getting ready for work in the morning.
- **Associated enterprises.** If you decide to raise your own oxen, you can easily complement the draft team with other enterprises. For example, the mothers of your draft steers

could be milked, and any surplus calves could be finished for beef.

The disadvantages of oxen include:

- **Susceptibility to heat.** In general, oxen like cooler climates than horses do. Working an ox team in very hot summer conditions can be detrimental to the health of the animals. (Using a Brahman or another zebu-influenced animal helps.)
- **Susceptibility to ice injuries.** The hoof structure of oxen is very different from that of horses. Oxen are more prone to ugly cuts when walking on icy surfaces.
- **Horns.** Most oxen have horns because horns can be necessary for holding a yoke in place, depending on the yoke design. However, horns can be dangerous to humans.
- **Slow pace.** Slow and steady describes the ox. While he may be able to outlast the horse, he will certainly move at a much slower pace. Besides the fact that fieldwork will take longer with oxen, some implements, such as no-till seed drills, may not operate properly at such low speeds.
- **Lack of precision.** Unlike draft horses, which are guided with bits and reins somewhat like saddle horses, oxen are trained to voice commands, and possibly to taps on the sides. Tight control cannot be attained with this system unless you are on your toes and your team is very obedient. While this lack of precision won't matter in many applications, such as pulling up stumps, it can be a problem when working in tight spaces, as when cultivating.

For truly heavy farm work, such as clearing land, the patient, hard-working ox is difficult to beat due to his impressive strength and great stamina. Keeping oxen is also a relatively low-cost way to enter the world of draft animals compared to some of the other options. Furthermore, if you are already keeping a family milk cow, you may be able to raise your own draft team without incurring any extra purchase costs!

Not everyone will enjoy working with oxen. Some people simply prefer the speed and mettle of a good horse team, and they will likely be very dissatisfied with the plodding pace of oxen. Oxen can also be cumbersome to handle in very small spaces or precise applications.

But for low-input systems, oxen are often a good fit.

Horses
The advantages of horses include:

- **Low cost of good animals.** Compared to some of the other draft animal options, horses are relatively easy to come by, which makes them less expensive. If you are looking at starting with a team that is already trained, you will particularly notice the price difference between horses and mules.
- **Relative ease of finding supplies and information.** Likewise, because horses are still commonly used for draft purposes, relatively speaking, finding resources should be quite doable. Even if you live in an area where equipment and expertise are not locally common, the Internet has made draft horse resources widely available.
- **Sizes for all purposes.** Whatever you want to pull, there is likely a horse of the right size to tackle the job. For a very small farm that produces nothing but vegetables and firewood, a pony may be all you need. For field work and logging, there are the tried-and-true draft horses. And then there's just about everything in between.
- **Docile temperament.** Although not as easy to train as oxen, compared to mules and donkeys, horses are far more amenable and less independent-minded. This is particularly true of the large draft breeds. The horse can also tolerate

more beginner mistakes than a mule can. A good draft horse may not be the fastest-learning animal on the planet, but it more than makes up for this in willingness.

- **Moderate heat tolerance.** While the horse cannot match the heat tolerance of the mule (can anything?), it is far more suitable for summer work than oxen. Horses are a good fit for all but the hottest climates.
- **Speed.** The horse is the fastest draft animal. If you are a farmer who likes to hustle, this may be the best bet for you.
- **Agility.** For tight corners and narrow rows of crops, equines have a maneuverability oxen cannot provide.
- **Dual-purpose transportation.** Of course, this depends on the size of the horse and the size of the rider, but many draft horses make surprisingly good saddle horses due to their kind, gentle dispositions.

The disadvantages of horses include:

- **Spookiness.** Out of all the draft animal options, horses are the most prone to panic. Needless to say, this can present some very dangerous situations. Breed choice (heavy breeds are the least skittish), careful selection of your new team, and proper training will all go a long way toward preventing mishaps.
- **Health issues.** Ideally, you will evaluate the soundness of any draft animal you are considering purchasing before bringing it home. That said, there are problems that can turn up after years of work, and injuries do occur. Horses are probably the most delicate of all the draft animals. Lameness and hoof problems are things to watch out for. There are also a number of genetic defects rampant in heavy breeds that, while not necessarily always fatal, may have a negative effect on their working ability.

- **Short working lifespan.** In keeping with their more delicate physique, horses often have shorter working lifespans than mules, although with proper care they may be able to match oxen.
- **Complex harness.** If you are interested in horses, you will need quite a bit of gear to make it all work. This means a greater up-front cost to get started, and a longer time spent harnessing in the morning before you can actually start work. The harness will also require considerably more maintenance than an ox yoke.
- **Feed needs.** Compared to the other draft animal species, horses require the most inputs to perform draft work. This means high-quality pasture for certain. Most working horses need supplemental feed, too, although not as much as you would expect given their size. They can also provide the power to grow their own grain.
- **Shoeing needs.** Fortunately, many draft horses do not require shoes to work. Unfortunately, many others do these days, primarily owing to soundness issues that have resulted from an emphasis on breeding heavy horses for looks. If you happen to have a team that needs shoes to avoid hoof problems, be prepared for hefty farrier bills—shoeing such large horses costs considerably more than shoeing mules or even saddle horses due to the large, specialized shoes that have to be made for them. For safety, some farriers also insist that draft horses be shod in stocks, a special restraint system something like a milking stanchion.
- **Less stamina.** Horses get tired more quickly than mules or oxen. If you expect to put in long, grueling days of work, you may want to consider another option.
- **Poor self-preservation instincts.** Donkeys and mules are pretty good at looking out for themselves and will simply refuse to be overworked. Those who choose to keep draft horses must do the monitoring. Keep an eye out for

exhaustion, overheating, colic, and founder from drinking too much water too quickly.

Some people keep draft horses because they love them—not entirely due to the beauty of horses, but often due to their personality. No mule, donkey, or ox will suffice in this case. The difference between a horse and a mule in loyalty, obedience, and trainability has been likened to the difference between a dog and a cat. Many people find dogs and horses easier to work with than cats and mules.

Furthermore, there is a great deal to be said for horses if you have no prior experience with draft animals. There is the temperament factor, as already mentioned, but there are many other considerations. Horses are often the easiest draft animals to come by, and there are more people with experience with horses available to mentor you. Harnesses for horses are also relatively easy to find.

But working horses require maintenance. They need high-quality pasture to meet the demands of farm work, and they may require supplemental feed at least seasonally. Shoeing them, while not always necessary, is also quite expensive. Care must be taken to prevent them from being overworked or going lame. And they have less stamina and shorter working lifespans than other draft animals. This adds up to make the horse a less-than-ideal fit for a truly low-input operation.

However, each individual has to weigh the pros and cons for himself:

- Are horses readily available to you?
- Are there the necessary resources, equipment, and knowledge in your area to make the project feasible?
- Would you benefit from working with a less independent-minded animal?
- Do you just love horses?

Depending on your answers to these questions, the benefits of horses may more than compensate for the negatives.

Mules

The advantages of mules include:

- **Superb heat tolerance.** Historically, the mule was the draft animal of choice in the Deep South due to its tolerance of heat and humidity.
- **Exceptional health and hardiness.** Few domestic animals are as tough as the mule. It rarely gets sick, and it almost never goes lame. It has a high degree of parasite resistance. Its hooves are exceptionally sturdy and generally don't require shoes unless it is being worked on pavement or very rocky ground.
- **Self-preservation instinct.** Mules have an unrivaled ability to look out for themselves. They rarely make themselves sick by eating or drinking too much all at once (except some mules from pony mares). They will not allow themselves to be overworked, either.
- **Calmness.** Mules are not prone to panic the way horses are. They may bolt out of willfulness, but rarely out of fear.
- **Low maintenance requirements.** Even when working, the mule requires very little supplemental feed (albeit more than a donkey). It does not require a pristine pasture or top-quality hay to stay in peak form. A draft mule is estimated to require about a third less feed than a working horse of the same size.
- **Longevity.** Draft mules have long working lifespans, up to nearly 20 years with proper care.
- **A balance of speed and stamina.** Speed and stamina are typically mutually exclusive, but the mule provides a very reasonable compromise. On a continuum with horses representing the most speed but least stamina and oxen

representing the most stamina but least speed, a mule would be right about at the balance point.

- **Sure-footedness.** Out of all the draft animals, mules are among the most sure of their footing, which is a plus on uneven ground or when working in tight quarters as when cultivating. There are two reasons for this. The first is that the mule has a narrower body and smaller hooves than a horse of the same size. The second is that it is always on the alert and acting as circumstances require.
- **Versatility.** Your draft mule can perform other work around the farm! It can be broken to ride just a like a horse. When not otherwise employed, it can also serve as a guardian for sheep and goats.

The disadvantages of mules include:

- **Prevalence of low-quality mules.** Too many people try to make a fast buck by breeding a cull jack to an inferior mare. While miracles do happen, in everyday life any mule that results from such a breeding is highly unlikely to exceed its parents in quality. Purchasing a mule requires adequate research to avoid picking up someone else's nightmare. A docile mare and positive human interaction from birth are two ingredients necessary to make a good mule.
- **Expense.** If you are starting out with a trained draft team (and you should give it some serious consideration if you are thinking about buying mules), a good mule team can be rather pricey.
- **Noise.** This should not be much of an issue for anyone who has enough land to be considering draft mules. That said, those considering a mule for tilling the garden in a more populated area may want to factor in the neighbors' feelings on the subject.

- **Training challenges.** Mules aren't exactly stubborn—they're just super independent, and they have an exceptional ability to spot a person who isn't really in control of a situation. But this independence, admirable though it may be in many situations, is not something most beginners want to deal with. Training mules for draft work is extremely challenging, and it requires a fair but firm hand, not to mention a considerable amount of time. Mistakes have long-term ramifications, and bad habits are extraordinarily difficult to weed out. (This is exactly why trained mules are so expensive.)
- **Complex harness.** Although there are differences, the harness used for mules is much like that used for horses with respect to complexity. It takes time to get it on the animals, and it requires regular maintenance.
- **Intelligent disobedience.** Even a well-trained mule will disobey if it feels the need, and it will insist on taking time to look over any and all dubious situations before proceeding. This is precisely due to its beneficial self-preservation instinct. That said, not everyone can handle the independence of mules. Horses are more like dogs; mules are more like cats (although not quite to the same degree as donkeys). There is a reason why many people would rather train dogs than cats!
- **Sterility.** The mule is the only draft animal that cannot replicate itself (with the caveat that most oxen are steers). Granted, your mule team should last for many years. But if you ever need to replace or expand it, you must purchase new animals or keep both horses and donkeys on hand to raise more yourself.

Mules can make a superb team for use in challenging conditions as they are the epitome of low-maintenance draft animals. Add to this their nice balance between speed and stamina, and you have an excellent choice for serious farm work.

However, there is a good reason that draft mules are not more common than they are—their temperament. Not everyone is going to enjoy working with mules. Beginners in particular may find mules to be too challenging when learning the ropes, even when dealing with a trained team. (And an untrained team can be a nightmare for all but the most dedicated and experienced farmers.)

Mules are superb in low-input farm situations. In hot climates they simply can't be beat. The question is whether or not you are one of those special people who can get along with a mule.

Donkeys

The advantages of donkeys include:

- **Low purchase cost.** Donkeys are typically very inexpensive, sometimes even free. A trained team may be a little more expensive (when locally available), but not by all that much.
- **Hardiness.** While donkeys are perhaps not quite as hardy as mules, they are extremely hardy nevertheless. Parasites should not present any great difficulties, and neither should overeating. Hoof and leg problems are also rare in donkeys.
- **Low feed costs.** Donkeys can thrive with very little feed (probably less than any other draft animal). They require supplemental feed if working hard on a regular basis, but less than a draft horse would. If they work only sporadically, they may not require any feed at all. Either way, donkeys do not require the same level of pasture quality that horses do.
- **Minimal hoof care.** Out of all the draft animals, donkeys require the least attention to their hooves. As long as they have room to walk around and access to some rougher ground that will wear down their hooves a bit, they should not require trimming. But even if your circumstances make trimming a necessity, shoes are not necessary for donkeys.

- **Simple harnesses.** Draft harnesses for donkeys and burros are typically quite simple, involving little more than a padded collar. This reduces the amount of time spent getting the donkey ready for work and then maintaining the harness.
- **Sure footing.** Donkeys are well suited to working on uneven fields or smaller properties with hard-to-reach corners.
- **Versatility.** A male work donkey could be kept for breeding mules (not recommended for beginners due to the difficult temperament of jacks). As an additional bonus, donkeys make good guard animals for sheep and goats. Some bigger donkeys can be ridden, although there aren't too many donkeys with the size and back strength for this purpose (a point in favor of the American Mammoth Jackstock breed).

The disadvantages of donkeys include:

- **Small size.** Most donkeys are too small for heavy draft work, and even a good-sized donkey cannot pull loads as heavy as an ox or mule can (although it might be able to outperform a horse of the same size). Nearly any donkey can pull a small cart loaded with firewood, but for heavier farm work you will want to consider a large donkey. Due to the donkey's smaller size, you may want to plan on two donkeys for every one horse that the job in question would require.
- **Variable availability.** While donkeys in general are rather common, draft donkeys are not. Your ability to find a sturdy draft donkey will depend on where you live.
- **Independent nature.** Donkeys can be difficult to train and work. They are more like cats than dogs when it comes to obedience, and they can be extremely wary, especially when young. Be prepared to earn their trust and to exercise a great deal of patience when dealing with potentially frightening situations. Also keep in mind that they will never allow themselves to be overworked or placed in danger. For most

beginners, starting with a trained team is probably the best bet.

In truly low-input systems, where little or no supplemental feed will be provided, a donkey may be your best choice. Not only are donkeys economical to keep, they are quite versatile, making them well suited to smaller farms. Even a miniature donkey can pull a small cart filled with vegetables or firewood.

Unfortunately, most donkeys are not big enough or sturdy enough for heavier draft work. For this purpose, you will likely want an American Mammoth Jackstock, which may or may not be readily available in your area. But if you are considering serious logging or other very heavy work, you may be happier with something bigger and therefore more powerful, such as an ox or a heavy-breed horse.

Also, not everyone gets along well with donkeys. Those who prefer a more docile animal will likely prefer oxen or horses. Donkeys are more focused on self-preservation—like a mule, but ever so much more so. But some people truly appreciate donkey intelligence. It's largely a matter of personal preference.

Goats

Really small-scale farmers should not overlook one of the more unconventional options—draft goats! If you only have a few acres and a cart for hauling vegetables and firewood, a larger draft animal may be overkill. Goats can pull carts and even skid some lighter logs. Further adding to their versatility, goats can clear brush when not working.

Female goats can pull their own bodyweight, while male goats can pull twice their bodyweight. Wethers are usually preferred for draft work because they are stronger than does but more tractable (and less smelly) than bucks.

Keeping a draft goat may sound far-fetched, but it really isn't. Goats are quite intelligent, and they love to be the center of attention, a combination that makes them nearly as trainable as dogs.

Comparison of Draft Animals

	Oxen	Horses	Mules	Donkeys	Goats
Availability of Draft Stock	Limited; better in New England area	Common	Moderate	Limited	Very limited
Price	Inexpensive	Extremely variable	Expensive	Very inexpensive (sometimes free)	Very inexpensive
Suitability for Small Acreages	No	Ponies and miniature horses	Miniature mules	Miniature donkeys	Yes
Preferred Climate	Cool but ice-free	Suitable for all but the hottest climates	Hot and humid	Warm and dry	Suitable for most dry climates
Disposition	Dependable	Docile but skittish	Calm but noisy and independent	Very independent	Trainable
Feed Needs	Low	High	Very low	Extremely low	Low unless lactating
Health	Mostly trouble-free	Prone to colic, founder, lameness, and genetic defects	Virtually trouble-free	Mostly trouble-free (needs shelter from rain)	Prone to internal parasites and hoof rot in wet weather
Working Lifespan	Moderate	Moderate	Excellent	Good	Moderate
Harnessing	Simple	Complex	Complex	Simple	Moderately simple
Strength (relative to size)	Good	Very good	Good	Excellent	Excellent
Speed	Slow	Very fast	Moderate	Moderate	Slow
Stamina	Excellent	Poor	Good	Good	Poor
Agility	Poor	Very good	Excellent	Very good	Excellent
Other Common Uses	None, but can be a good use for dairy calves	Riding	Riding, livestock guardian	Livestock guardian, breeding mules	Clearing brush

9. What is the strongest draft animal?

There is a common stereotype that the ox is the strongest draft animal, much stronger than a horse. Actually, when pulling a wheeled load all day, the horse can pull 1-1/2 times its own weight, while an ox can pull its own weight. The reason that oxen are perceived as stronger than horses is that they have much greater stamina. They can work longer hours, and don't tend to lose condition when worked daily like horses. This is why the ox was preferred in the Oregon Trail days (plus, heavy draft breeds were not as common in the United States back then).

Actually, the strongest draft animal commonly in use is the donkey. On a smooth surface, a donkey can pull a wheeled load that is twice its bodyweight.

It is also interesting to note that among less common draft animals dogs probably hold the record for pulling power relative to size. In short bursts, dogs can pull over 20 times their own bodyweight! For long distances, properly conditioned sled dogs pull at least twice their own weight, with dogs trained specifically for freight sledding pulling more than that.

Oxen

10. What is an ox?

An ox is a bovine specifically trained for draft work. Generally, the term *ox* is applied to mature cattle rather than calves, as a good ox must have reached its full size and muscling and must have full understanding of the basic commands. Also, most oxen are steers, or castrated males. Cows and bulls are occasionally used for draft purposes, but the steer's docility makes it the ideal animal for work.

Any cattle breed can technically serve as an ox. However, sturdy, docile (but reasonably intelligent) animals are preferred. Dairy and dual-purpose breeds are most commonly used due to their athleticism, but some beef steers are also suitable.

11. How much can a single heifer pull?

Assuming they are trained and in peak condition, oxen of all types can pull their own bodyweight at a walking pace over long distances.

A mature American Milking Devon cow will weigh 1,000 to 1,200 pounds, but as a young heifer, she might weigh only 550 to 660 pounds. This would be about the weight she could theoretically pull.

Mostly likely, though, our hypothetical heifer would not be able to pull quite this much weight yet, as she would still be growing and would be starting to put more energy into reproduction.

12. How far can oxen travel in a day?

Oregon Trail diaries suggest that an ox team could average about 12 to 15 miles per day. If the terrain was level and the team was in good health, they might make as many as 20 miles per day. If the terrain became exceptionally steep and rocky, causing the animals to become footsore, they might only make five to eight miles a day, or even less.

13. How long can oxen live?

This depends on the care the oxen receive, but also on the breed. These days, many cattle are considered old by the time they are six to eight years old. Most draft oxen, however, come from heritage breeds, which tend to live longer due to their greater health and hardiness. Heritage-breed cattle often live into their teens, and some into their twenties and even beyond.

However, there is no guarantee a working ox will be able to live this long. People who raise oxen as dual-purpose beef animals may only work them until they are seven or eight years old. Those who use their oxen strictly for draft purposes may opt to keep them past the age of 10, assuming they are sound and healthy. A working life does take its toll on feet and legs, so draft oxen may not always be able to live with comfort as long as the breed average would suggest.

14. Can you ride oxen?

Yes, you can, but this requires additional training.

First, you will want to choose a sound steer with sturdy legs and a docile disposition. He should have been accustomed to human contact from birth. (Good oxen should meet these requirements, anyway.)

If you intend to use your ox for riding as well as for draft purposes, you will want to start his training at a young age. He will need to be taught to lead with the rope halter first. Put the halter on him, then pet him and praise him for accepting it. Once this is accepted as a matter of course, take him to a safe pen, add the lead rope and let him drag it along the ground; if he steps on the rope, he will learn that he is more comfortable yielding to the pressure than fighting it. At this point, you can try leading him around the pen. If he resists, tie him to a sturdy cattle panel and step back. Let him pull against it for a while until he realizes that resistance is futile.

As he gets used to the idea, you can gradually introduce him to the concept of carrying a person, starting by leaning on his back. As long as he is big enough to safely carry your weight, you should eventually be able to climb on. (If you plan to ride him with a saddle, introduce that first.)

You can get as advanced with your training as you would like at this point. Some trainers find that clicker training and treats work wonders when teaching steers to respond to rein cues. Others enjoy the results they get from dressage training a steer as they would a horse.

Once you have trained your ox to be ridden, you will probably be amazed at all he can do. Riding steers are great for pleasure riding, but they can also be used to work cattle.

Horses

15. How much can a draft horse pull?

When working all day, a horse can pull a dead weight that is about a tenth of its weight. When the load has wheels, the horse can pull about 1-1/2 times its bodyweight. Under optimal conditions (e.g., working on smooth, level pavement), the horse may even be able to pull two or three times its own weight.

Things get even more interesting when you start teaming horses together. A pair of horses can actually pull three times their combined bodyweight on the road. The reason for this is that, by teaming the horses, each horse individually has to apply less force to overcome friction.

For short distances, one horse may be able to pull 10 to 15 times its weight. But this is typically only seen in pulling contests, not in everyday work.

16. Are draft horses gentle?

Most draft horse breeds are known for their natural gentleness and docility. (A wild draft animal is not terribly useful.)

However, there is a phenomenon among some draft horses, particularly those owned by inexperienced handlers, known as "Gentle Giant Syndrome." Gentle Giant Syndrome is caused by an assumption that all big draft horses are tractable and that there is no need to establish a respectful relationship between horse and human. The symptoms of Gentle Giant Syndrome include a whole host of disrespectful behaviors, including fidgeting, refusing to accept grooming and shoeing, and the like.

Also, even heavy-breed horses are more prone to panic than other types of draft animals. Choosing calm, docile horses and training them properly is a must for preventing accidents.

A few high-strung individuals exist in some breeds. You will want to evaluate the temperament of the individual horse you are interested in before purchasing it, regardless of breed.

So, while the vast majority of draft horses are quite gentle, you will want to pick your team wisely and then pay attention to building a bond based on trust and respect.

17. Can draft horses be ridden?

Because they are typically docile, draft horses make excellent mounts for larger riders. Be prepared for the following challenges, however:

- Finding a saddle big enough for that broad back may be difficult.
- Mounting a draft horse requires athleticism.
- Draft horses prefer to walk, so don't expect much speed.

Mules

18. Could the smaller and more careful-footed mule be better suited for cultivation work than other draft animals?

Mules beat oxen for cultivation work quite easily due to the precise control you can achieve with a harness and lines versus a yoke and goad. However, mules are also more sure-footed than horses, which makes them particularly superb for this delicate task.

19. Might a mule team be more inclined to stand still and wait for clearer instructions from a beginning teamster, rather than run away from a perceived danger?

First off, mules are among the most calm and level-headed draft animals. They are far less prone to spookiness and panic than horses. A secure, well-trained mule is curious, even playful. It can keep its cool in tough situations, and it will reward its handler's attentions with devoted affection. Female (molly) mules are quite stable even when in season, rarely displaying the unpredictable behavior of a mare. If a mule bolts, it will most likely be an act of rebellion rather than an act of fear.

However, when faced with perceived danger, mules trust their personal safety to no one. This has given rise to the mule stubbornness legend. There is far more to mule nature than stubbornness; obstinacy is usually a response to a perceived threat. If they feel the need to balk or run, mules will not stop to consider the farmer's instructions, especially if they do not have a solid trust-based relationship with him.

When working with mules, you will want to give them time to think things through. They do not blindly obey orders. New tasks and routines must be explained to them patiently but firmly. Likewise, they must be given time to accept strangers. Incautious advances may be received with a deadly kick.

A mule never forgets. Mistreatment or a frightening experience when the mule is young will color its disposition for life. It will hold a grudge and can be a dangerously calculating enemy.

Unconventional Draft Animals

20. Can a llama pull a cart?

Yes! If you are looking for a draft animal guaranteed to attract a curious crowd, look no further! Llama carting is considered a highly addictive pastime by some and a competitive sport by others. Llamas can provide personal transportation, perform in parades, and even participate in llama-driving shows. Yet they are also among the most low-maintenance draft animals.

Be careful to pay attention to fit and quality when purchasing a harness for a llama. Llamas come in many shapes and sizes, so getting the right gear can be a challenge. A harness and cart specifically designed for llamas is highly recommended, as equipment for ponies is too heavy and does not give the llama enough flexibility to turn or change gaits.

Each new experience must be introduced carefully, however. Llamas that have been pushed before they are ready are known to protest in dramatic style. They tend to accept carting more quickly if they see another, more experienced llama demonstrating it first. Also, give them time to examine their new cart thoroughly before trying to harness them to it.

On the other hand, be aware that llamas are quite intelligent and will not tolerate meaningless repetition. They do not like going endlessly in circles, and they often are bored by working in arenas. Llamas prefer to work in a variety of outdoor settings.

21. Can alpacas pull carts?

They can, but greater care must be taken than with llamas. Alpacas are much more delicate and can only pull about 25% of their body weight.

Alpacas are also more timid than llamas, which can be a disadvantage in draft work. However, they are also more docile.

One advantage alpacas have as draft animals is that they can serve as dual-purpose livestock thanks to their valuable fiber.

22. When might a draft dog be preferable to other small draft animals, such as ponies and mules?

If you already have a pet dog on hand strong enough and willing enough for the job you have in mind, perhaps the most obvious thing to do is to train him for draft work. (Who knows, it might just be the energy outlet he needs.)

If you are thinking about acquiring a dog, there are still several advantages:

- Dogs are remarkably strong for their size.
- Even if you live in the city, you can probably still have one.
- They don't require acres of space to graze, just a yard for exercise.
- They are pretty straightforward to train and care for.
- They can serve as watchdogs in their spare time.

Chapter 3
Choosing a Breed

O nce you know what species you would like to work with, it is time to choose a breed. There are many different breeds of oxen, horses, and other draft animals. This is because mankind has developed these distinct breeds for hundreds, even thousands, of years to fit specific environmental conditions and production systems. The breed that will work best for you will be the one that was developed with a similar situation in mind.

As a side note, there aren't exactly breeds of mule. A mule's breed is typically described as the breed of the horse involved; for example, a Belgian mule had a Belgian horse for a parent. Mules commonly inherit their temperament and a good degree of their physical prowess from their horse parent, which means that prospective mule owners may want to become familiar with horse breeds.

Ox Breeds

23. Which ox breed is best?

The best ox breed for you will be the one that most closely fits your needs:

- What are your environmental conditions like?
- What temperament will you be most satisfied with?
- What is readily available to you?
- Are there any other purposes you have in mind for your cattle besides draft work?

There is a reason why so many cattle breeds (hundreds, in fact) have developed over time. Breeds were selected by man and nature to fit varying purposes, production systems, environmental conditions, and more. There is a reason why furry Highland cattle originated in cold, windswept Scotland, while the heat-tolerant zebu breeds inhabited India from an early date. There is also a reason why small farmers raising a milk cow for the family would not want a high-production industrial dairy cow!

The best breed for you will meet your needs in five basic areas:

- **Purpose.** Obviously you are interested in draft work, but would you like your cattle to produce beef and/or dairy, as well? How about other purposes, such as land clearing, hides, or even yarn?
- **Scale.** How many acres of pasture do you have, and what is the recommended stocking rate in your area? Also, if you will keep dual-purpose cattle, what level of beef or milk production do you need?
- **Environment.** What is your climate like? What forage resources do you have, and how does their quality vary seasonally? What diseases and parasites are common in your area? Will your oxen be working under challenging conditions, such as rough terrain, deep mud, or high humidity?
- **Marketing plan.** Will you be raising and selling steers for oxen? How do your oxen fit into your agritourism enterprise? If your cattle will be dual-purpose, who will be buying your

meat or milk, and what are their expectations? How will you promote and distribute any of these products and services?

- **Personal preference.** Do you want smarter, faster oxen, or will you be more comfortable with docile but slower cattle to start out? Do you have any other personal expectations, such as the appearance of your team? What breeds are you most strongly drawn to?

Before you even begin researching individual cattle breeds, you might want to write down your objectives in these areas.

The following is an overview of the most common ox breeds in the United States, along with their advantages and disadvantages relative to draft work. Note that crosses of these breeds are also usually suitable for draft purposes.

Ayrshire
The Ayrshire is a moderate-sized and fairly active breed, which makes it a good general-purpose work ox for diversified farms.

Pros:

- Adaptability to a wide variety of climates.
- Low maintenance requirements.
- A knack at rustling a living on rough pastures.
- Moderate size suitable for all-around farm and woods work.
- More muscle than most dairy breeds.
- Soundness.
- Longevity.

Cons:

- Strong personality, which may be difficult for beginners to handle.

Brahman

Although the Brahman is not a common choice for draft work in the United States, similar zebu breeds are preferred for draft purposes across the world, particularly in hot, humid climates.

Pros:

- Low prices, especially outside of the South.
- Extreme hardiness.
- Heat tolerance.
- Resistance to intense sunlight.
- Parasite resistance.
- Active foraging nature.
- Ability to cope with poor and inconsistent grazing.
- Willingness to eat cactus, yucca, and other plants many European breeds won't touch.
- Longevity.
- Outstanding hybrid vigor of crossbred steers.

Cons:

- Reduced availability in Northern latitudes.
- Tendency to jump fences.
- Active, somewhat shy personality, difficult for inexperienced owners to handle.
- Tendency to become nervous or aggressive if handled roughly or infrequently.
- Late maturity.

Brown Swiss

Although it is slow, the Brown Swiss is strong, calm, and relatively trouble-free, making it a good choice for beginners.

Pros:

- Affordable prices.
- Adaptability.
- Calm, forgiving disposition, easy for beginners to handle.
- Fast growth.
- Strength.
- Sound feet and legs.
- Longevity.

Cons:

- Large size—not suited to smaller properties.
- Very slow working pace.

Chianina

The Chianina was bred in Italy for draft purposes. While it is not a common choice on working farms in America today, it can excel in competitive pulling.

Pros:

- Hardiness.
- Adaptability to most climates.
- Resistance to parasites.
- Decent foraging ability.
- Exceptional size and strength—ideally suited to competitive pulling.
- Longevity.
- Good growth and hybrid vigor of crossbred steers.

Cons:

- Difficulty of containment due to large size.
- Large appetite.
- Poor performance under minimal management.

- Very excitable temperament, ranging from nervous to aggressive.
- Low trainability.
- Late maturity.
- Poor athleticism of beef-cross cattle.

Devon

There are two types of Devon today—a beef type and the American Milking Devon, which is the historic ox of the pioneers. The latter is still used for draft work today. Although its high energy levels may challenge beginners, it is hard to beat as an all-around farm worker.

Pros:

- Moderately small size, suitable for smaller acreages and easier on pastures.
- Hardiness.
- Adaptability to most climates and pasture conditions, particularly drought.
- Resistance to external parasites.
- Resistance to many diseases.
- Ability to thrive on minimal inputs and rough forage.
- Strong foraging instinct.
- Plucky, intelligent personality.
- Suitability for all-around farm work.
- Great strength relative to size.
- Great endurance when working.
- Fast working pace.
- Longevity.
- Good temperament and hybrid vigor of crossbred steers.

Cons:

- Scarcity.

- Ability to outwit inexperienced trainers.
- Energy level difficult for beginners to handle.

Dexter

The Dexter is commonly thought of as a hobby farm ox, and its small size certainly does make it ideal for this setting. However, its strength and pluck make it suitable for more challenging situations, as well.

Pros:

- Size that fits well onto smaller farms.
- Low impact on land and fences.
- Adaptability.
- Hardiness.
- Exceptionally low maintenance requirements.
- Aggressive foraging and browsing instincts.
- Docility and trainability if handled regularly from a young age.
- Determination when pulling heavy loads.
- Fast working pace.
- Sure-footedness.
- Ability to work in tight quarters, such as thick stands of trees.
- Heavy muscling relative to size.
- Soundness.
- Longevity.

Cons:

- Tendency to act up if not handled regularly from a young age.

Dutch Belted

With its low maintenance requirements and great docility, the Dutch Belted is an exceptional ox for beginners. Unfortunately, it can be very hard to find in many areas.

Pros:

- Consistent quality.
- Adaptability.
- Hardiness.
- Good foraging instincts.
- Ability to maintain body condition on limited resources.
- Easygoing but smart temperament—well suited to beginners.
- Early maturity.
- Amazing longevity.
- Significant hybrid vigor of crossbred steers.

Cons:

- Scarcity.

Guernsey

The Guernsey is a moderate-sized ox with a good disposition that can pull its weight on smaller farms.

Pros:

- Moderate size, ideally suited to homesteads and small farms.
- Adaptability to most climates.
- Excellent grazing instincts.
- Ability to thrive on poor land.
- Steady temperament suitable for beginners
- Early maturity.
- Longevity.

Cons:

- Relative scarcity, and therefore expense.
- Amazing ability as an escape artist.
- Somewhat delicate health.

Hereford

The horned Hereford is still used as a draft ox in Canada, although it is less common for this purpose in the United States.

Pros:

- Availability.
- Reasonable prices for horned steers in many areas.
- Great hardiness.
- Extreme heat and cold tolerance.
- Ability to thrive on forage alone.
- Extremely calm disposition, which is easy on both people and equipment.
- Early maturity.
- Longevity.

Cons:

- Wide variability in soundness, although this is improving.
- Tendency to get too fat unless kept on a strictly grass-based diet.

Highland

For self-sufficiency, the good-looking Highland is hard to beat. Keep in mind, however, that it will overheat easily due to its shaggy hair.

Pros:

- Availability.
- Affordable prices.
- Striking appearance.
- Remarkable tolerance of long-distance shipping.
- Extreme hardiness.
- Exceptional cold tolerance.
- Hardiness against predators.

- Self-sufficiency.
- Small size that is easier on pastures and allows for higher stocking rates.
- Ability to thrive on poor pastures.
- Taste for undesirable weeds and brush, including cedar and poison ivy.
- Temperament suitable for beginners, provided it is handled regularly from a young age.
- Intelligence.
- Active working pace.
- Longevity.
- Great hybrid vigor in crossbred steers.

Cons:

- Variable quality; some bloodlines have issues with health and temperament.
- Poor heat tolerance, especially if working.
- Strong aversion to confinement.
- Long hair, which may gather mud.
- High-maintenance hooves.
- Trouble with ticks and lice in hot weather.
- Challenges of transporting and working with steers with particularly long horns.
- Tendency to become quite wild unless handled regularly from a young age.
- Late maturity.

Holstein

Due to their availability and good nature, Holsteins and Holstein crosses are often the easiest way for novices to enter the world of draft animals.

Pros:

- Availability.
- Affordable prices.
- Agreeability.
- Early maturity.
- Excellent suitability of most Holstein crosses for draft due to size and good disposition.

Cons:

- Poor heat tolerance.
- Extremely high maintenance requirements.
- Incredible appetite.
- Inability to perform on poor-quality pastures.
- Short lifespan.

Jersey

Jersey steers are readily available, making them an easy entry point for many. Keep in mind, however, that they are not as strong as other breeds.

Pros:

- Availability.
- Reasonable prices.
- Ease of putting together a matched team.
- Excellent heat tolerance.
- Excellent grazing instincts.
- Small size, which is easier on pastures.
- Remarkable intelligence.
- Early maturity.
- Fast working pace.
- Longevity when given good care.

Cons:

- Variability in areas such as maintenance requirements.
- Poor hardiness.
- Poor tolerance of extreme cold.
- Ability to outwit humans.
- Excitable, headstrong disposition.
- Limited strength as a draft ox due to small size and light muscling.

Randall

Although hard to come by in most parts of the country, the Randall is a traditional multipurpose ox, genetically the same as the oxen used on New England farms a mere century ago.

Pros:

- Striking appearance.
- Hardiness.
- Ability to thrive in cool climates.
- Good disease and parasite resistance.
- Self-reliance.
- Extremely low maintenance requirements.
- Docile temperament of steers.
- Excellent trainability.
- Excellent memory.
- Moderately brisk working pace.
- Longevity.

Cons:

- Scarcity.
- Variability, although this can increase its versatility.
- Poor heat tolerance.
- Energy level difficult for beginners to handle.

Shorthorn

The milking and heritage types of Shorthorn (not the beef type) are versatile, trainable work oxen, particularly useful in cool climates.

Pros:

- Adaptability to cool and temperate climates.
- Ability to thrive on forage alone (heritage type).
- Mild, trainable disposition.
- Early maturity.
- Suitability for just about any draft application.
- Good muscling.
- Health and soundness (heritage type).
- Longevity (heritage type).

Cons:

- Unsuitability for extremely hot climates.
- Poor performance on fescue pastures.
- Obesity when fed grain.
- Susceptibility of milking type to many health problems and genetic defects.
- Low hybrid vigor of Milking Shorthorn crosses due to extensive Holstein influence.

Texas Longhorn

The Texas Longhorn is an attractive and self-sufficient ox, although it can be a real handful for beginners.

Pros:

- Availability.
- Hardiness.
- Adaptability to extremes of either heat or cold.
- Self-reliance.

- Higher stocking rates due to forage efficiency.
- Exceptional parasite and disease resistance.
- Ability to ward off predators.
- Ability to thrive on grass alone.
- Willingness to eat invasive weeds.
- Remarkable intelligence.
- Plucky temperament.
- Athleticism.
- Exceptional longevity.
- Excellent hybrid vigor when crossbred.

Cons:

- High prices for quality steers.
- Ability as an escape artist.
- Tendency to become wild unless handled frequently from a young age.
- Ability to outwit humans.
- Active temperament, difficult for beginners to handle.
- Danger and difficulty of handling cattle with extremely long horns.

24. What are some common ox breeds around the four-state region of Missouri, Kansas, Iowa, and Nebraska?

You may be hard-pressed to find trained oxen or cattle bred specifically for draft work in this area (although you might have some success in Missouri).

However, you should have no problem finding steers from one of these breeds:

- Ayrshire.
- Brown Swiss.

- Charolais.
- Chianina.
- Devon (American Milking).
- Dexter.
- Guernsey.
- Hereford (horned).
- Highland.
- Holstein.
- Jersey.
- Randall.
- Shorthorn (Milking and Heritage).
- Texas Longhorn.

25. Can any of the other breeds such as Longhorns or Brahmans match the speed of Devons?

The American Milking Devon is definitely one of the liveliest ox breeds, making it a superb choice for someone who likes to work at a fairly brisk pace. Few breeds can beat the Devon for working speed.

Other breeds known for speed, albeit to a lesser degree, include:

- Ayrshire.
- Brahman.
- Dexter.
- Highland.
- Jersey.
- Texas Longhorn.

Horse Breeds

26. What are the draft horse breeds?

When you think of "draft horse breeds," the first thing that comes to mind is probably the heavy breeds. These are the ones best suited to pulling plows, clearing land, and other strenuous work. However, light horses and ponies can do lighter farm work, as well. They may not be suited for logging or pulling stumps, but they can pull carts, plow lighter soils, skid firewood, and the like.

The following are some of the favorite draft horse breeds of all sizes.

American Cream Draft

The American Cream Draft is a moderate-sized draft horse with a unique appearance bred specifically for farm work in America.

Pros:

- Unique and attractive appearance.
- Flashy gait.
- Moderate size, easier for many to keep.
- Easygoing, trustworthy nature well suited to beginners.
- Good work ethic.
- Sure-footedness.
- Muscularity.
- Strong legs and hooves.

Cons:

- Extreme scarcity.

Belgian

If you are looking for a no-frills workhorse for heavy draft purposes, whether that is farming, logging, or competing, the Belgian may be exactly what you need.

Pros:

- Ability to withstand shipping stress.
- Relatively low maintenance requirements.
- Early maturity.
- Safe, stable personality.
- Impressive muscling.
- Heavyweight pulling power.
- Ability to work for long periods of time.

Cons:

- Can be expensive to purchase.

Canadian

The Canadian was long the all-around farm horse of settlers in Canada and in the northern United States, and it can still excel in a diverse farm setting today.

Pros:

- Suitability for cold climates.
- Hardiness.
- Resistance to many diseases.
- Easy-keeping tendencies.
- Sure-footedness.
- Calm, docile, but spirited temperament.
- Strength.
- Endurance.
- Resistance to lameness, partly due to sturdy hooves.

Cons:

- Scarcity.

Cleveland Bay

The Cleveland Bay is a harness horse first and foremost. It can be driven for pleasure or competition, but it can also thrive on moderate farm work.

Pros:

- Uniformity (helpful for putting together matching teams).
- Adaptability to many climates.
- Hardiness.
- Sure-footedness.
- Endurance.
- Agility.
- Strength.
- Longevity.
- Strong ability to pass working traits on to crossbred offspring.

Cons:

- Scarcity.
- Need for experienced training and handling due to high intelligence and short attention span.
- Slow maturity.
- Poor ability to pass soundness on to crossbred offspring.

Clydesdale

The Clydesdale is probably one of the most famous draft horse breeds. Its gorgeous appearance makes it a favorite, ideally suited for work in the public eye.

Pros:

- Availability.
- Relatively low purchase cost.
- Impressive appearance, making it an excellent choice for parade and promotional hitches.
- Hardiness, particularly in cold weather.
- Safety around children and people inexperienced with horses due to gentle nature.
- Impressive strength.
- Brisk pace.
- Longevity.

Cons:

- Space requirements.
- Hefty appetite.
- Need for a special high-fat diet for optimal health and performance.
- High-maintenance feathering on legs.

Connemara

The Connemara is a versatile pony with a pleasing disposition and the ability to thrive on few inputs.

Pros:

- Relatively low cost.
- Resistance to cold, wet weather.
- Low feed requirements.
- Strong foraging instinct.
- Hardiness.
- Safe personality.
- Sure-footedness.
- Speed.
- Stamina.

- Agility.
- Longevity.

Cons:

- Late maturity.

Friesian

The stately Friesian is strong and obliging, but it lacks the physical and mental stamina necessary to be an ideal farm workhorse. Instead, it is better suited to work involving the public.

Pros:

- Fair availability.
- Stately appearance, particularly suited to funerals.
- Economical feed requirements relative to size.
- Strength.

Cons:

- Extravagant prices (yearlings are more affordable).
- Extensive grooming requirements.
- Need for experienced handling due to unique personality and many health issues.
- Slow pace.
- Lack of stamina.
- Short lifespan.

Haflinger

Although pony-like in size and mischief, the Haflinger is actually a horse with the ability to be a valuable farmhand for those equal to its antics.

Pros:

- Affordability.
- Low feed needs.
- Small size, easy to care for.
- Sweet, docile disposition toward people who have earned its respect.
- Good work ethic.
- Sure-footedness.
- Strength.
- Sturdy build.
- Impressive strength relative to size.

Cons:

- Grooming requirements, especially in muddy locations.
- Tendency toward obesity.
- Difficulty of training due to stubbornness and ability to outthink inexperienced handlers.
- Susceptibility to arthritis.

Icelandic Horse

The Icelandic Horse is usually considered an extremely comfortable saddle horse, but the hardiness and strength that make it ideal for riding also make it a good candidate for light draft work in colder climates.

Pros:

- Extreme hardiness.
- Extreme cold tolerance.
- Ability to live outdoors all year.
- Low maintenance requirements.
- Foraging ability.
- Easy-to-handle disposition.
- Sure-footedness.

- Athleticism.
- Impressive strength.
- Stamina.
- Longevity.

Cons:

- Slow maturity.

Miniature Horse

For really small farms, the Miniature Horse can double as a friendly pet and a garden helper. Although it cannot work on the same scale as bigger horses, it can still pull a small cart with tools, produce, firewood, and other light loads.

Pros:

- Suitability for small properties.
- Adaptability to cold weather.
- Economical feed requirements.
- Hardiness.
- Ease of handling.
- Strength.
- Stamina.
- Longevity.

Cons:

- High prices, although pet-quality geldings can be quite affordable.
- Reduced heat tolerance.
- Susceptibility to external parasites due to thick coat.
- Special health needs (clipping, dental care, weight monitoring, etc.).

Morgan

The Morgan is a traditional American all-around farm breed. Morgans that have been bred for practical qualities can still be a valuable asset to any small farmer or homesteader.

Pros:

- Availability.
- Low feed requirements.
- Hardiness.
- Suitability for beginners due to excellent temperament.
- Great stamina.
- Exceptional strength.
- Longevity.

Cons:

- High prices in some regions.
- Prevalence of Morgans bred for show rather than work.
- Relatively late maturity.

Norwegian Fjord

Although not the easiest breed to find in the United States, the Norwegian Fjord is a small, attractive horse noted for its hardiness and its versatility.

Pros:

- Suitability for challenging environments.
- Hardiness.
- Low feed requirements.
- Friendly, sensible disposition.
- Tendency to retain training even after long periods of inactivity.
- Work ethic.

- Sturdiness.
- Longevity.

Cons:

- Scarcity.
- High prices.
- Reduced heat tolerance.
- Headstrong personality.

Percheron

The Percheron excels at any task requiring strength and size. It can provide draft power for the farm or the woodlot, but its graceful bearing makes it a good choice for pleasure driving, as well.

Pros:

- Attractive appearance.
- Low grooming requirements compared to other draft breeds.
- Relatively low feed requirements.
- Hardiness.
- Strength.
- Stamina.

Cons:

- Difficult temperament for novice horse owners to handle in some bloodlines.

Shetland

The Shetland can be more than just a pasture pet! Putting a Shetland to work can help you with the chores and help your pony stay slim.

Pros:

- Availability.

- Affordable prices for the classic type.
- Extreme hardiness.
- Resistance to harsh winter weather.
- Ability to thrive on minimal feed.
- Sure-footedness.
- Endurance.
- Amazing strength for its size.
- Longevity.

Cons:

- Expense of the modern type.
- Ability as an escape artist.
- Tendency toward weight problems.
- Need for ample mental exercise.
- Somewhat difficult personality.

Shire

The Shire is noted for its great size. Unfortunately, this may make it difficult to keep for many farmers, although it can be a favorite for show hitches.

Pros:

- Easy-to-handle personality.
- Good work ethic.
- Flashy gait.
- Extreme strength.
- Endurance.
- Surprising athleticism.

Cons:

- Relative scarcity.
- High grooming requirements.

- High maintenance costs due to large size; needs ample feed, large shoes, a roomy stall, etc.
- High impact on pastures.
- High-maintenance feathering on legs.
- Slow working pace.

Suffolk Punch

The Suffolk Punch may be rather plain in appearance, but it is a true workhorse with the will to carry on no matter what.

Pros:

- Uniformity, which makes it easy to find a matching team.
- Heat tolerance.
- Hardiness.
- Surprisingly low feed requirements for a heavy horse.
- Lack of feathering—ideal for wet, heavy soils.
- Shorter stature than most draft breeds, making it easier to groom and harness.
- Early maturity.
- Unequaled work ethic.
- Power.
- Tremendous stamina.
- Fast working pace.
- Exceptional longevity.

Cons:

- Scarcity.

27. Which draft horse is the biggest?

The Shire is on average the largest draft horse breed, measuring anywhere from 16 to 19 hands tall.

The tallest horse in history was a Shire from England named Sampson, although he was later nicknamed Mammoth. He measured just over 21-1/2 hands tall in 1850 (he was four years old at the time).

However, the tallest horse living at the time of this writing according to Guinness World Records is Big Jake, a Belgian Draft. He stands just over 20-1/2 hands tall!

28. What horse breeds may be used for logging?

For this purpose, a heavy horse breed will be desired, as these breeds are noted for their size, strength, robust legs, and steady dispositions. Horses still used for logging include:

- Belgian.
- Percheron.
- Suffolk Punch.

Although much smaller, Haflingers also have the sturdy build necessary for logging, making them another candidate, although they will be limited in the size of the logs they can pull.

(As a side note, big mules of draft horse descent can also be used for this purpose.)

29. How much work can a team of miniature horses do?

Miniature horses are typically used for recreational driving, but they can do some light work on a small homestead. Obviously, the work should be matched to the horse's size to avoid injury or accident. As long as this is taken into consideration, a miniature horse can be surprisingly useful on a small scale.

One miniature horse can pull a small stone boat and skid light logs of firewood diameter. It can even pull a scaled-down plow or cultivator to use in the garden. With a miniature horse cart in tow, it could haul vegetables, compost, feed, firewood, tools, or whatever else your ingenuity can devise.

Obviously, a whole team would be even more versatile.

Other Draft Animals

30. Which goats are good for draft?

Any breed or gender of goat can be taught to pull, provided it likes people and is fully grown. For your goat's safety, don't expect it to pull a load until it is one to two years old, although some basic training can and should occur before this age. Wethers are generally preferred due to their docility (and the absence of buck odor). Even a Pygmy goat can pull small loads, although for serious farm work a larger breed is obviously more useful. Larger dairy breeds are most commonly used. Meat breeds are strong enough, but they tend to be less energetic.

The following are some of the better goat breeds for draft work purposes.

Alpine
The Alpine is a large, sturdy goat, making it a common choice for carting. However, its strong-willed temperament can make it a challenge to train.

Pros:

- Adaptability to all but wet climates.
- Hardiness.
- Early maturity.
- Size.

- Strength.
- Longevity.

Cons:

- Personality unsuited for confinement.
- Ability as an escape artist.
- Unsuitability for wet climates.
- High feed requirements.
- Stubbornness.

Boer

The Boer goat is certainly sturdy enough to pull a considerable amount of weight. It is a less common choice for draft work, however, as it tends to have lower energy levels than many goat breeds.

Pros:

- Respect for most mesh and electric fencing.
- Adaptability to both extreme heat and cold when provided with a simple shelter.
- Strong instinct to graze even during adverse weather.
- Ability to thrive on brushy pasture.
- Disease resistance.
- Easy-to-handle disposition.
- Fast growth rate.
- Heavy muscling.
- Marked ability to transmit docility, growth rate, and bone substance to crossbred offspring.

Cons:

- Abundance of poor-quality specimens.

- High feed requirements of goats from show lines (not usually a problem in goats bred for commercial production).
- Susceptibility to internal parasites.
- Laziness.

Kiko

The Kiko goat is sometimes used for draft work, although this is not common due to its almost feral disposition. However, if you take the time to tame one from birth, it will reward you by requiring almost no special care.

Pros:

- Adaptability to most climates.
- Hardiness.
- Very low maintenance requirements.
- Excellent health.
- Parasite resistance.
- Fast growth.
- Strength.

Cons:

- Ability as an escape artist (even better than the "average goat").
- Wild disposition (if used for work, must be handled regularly from birth).

LaMancha

The LaMancha is most famous for its tiny ears. However, its sweet disposition and remarkable trainability make it suitable for lighter carting applications.

Pros:

- Availability.
- Adaptability to even the harshest climates.
- Few health problems.
- Exceptionally easy-to-handle temperament.
- Trainability (probably the best of any goat breed).

Cons:

- Strange appearance; visitors will ask what happened to the ears.
- Ability as an escape artist.
- Special hygiene requirements (regular cleaning of earwax to avoid infection).
- Smaller size.

Nubian

Although it is pretty hardheaded, the Nubian has the size and strength to make a very useful draft animal for a patient trainer.

Pros:

- Tolerance of most climates, particularly hot ones.
- Few health problems.
- Tendency to bond readily with humans.
- Patience with children.
- Trainability.
- Rapid growth.
- Heavy muscling.
- Longevity.

Cons:

- Noise.
- Exceptional ability as an escape artist.
- Susceptibility to frostbitten ears.

- Undershot bite, which can make grazing difficult (better suited to browsing trees and shrubs).
- Stubbornness when asked to do something outside the normal routine.

Oberhasli

The Oberhasli is another highly trainable goat breed. Unfortunately, its scarcity and smaller size make it less common for carting.

Pros:

- Adaptability to many climates, particularly cold ones.
- Feed efficiency.
- Hardiness.
- Steady disposition.
- Trainability.
- Strength.

Cons:

- Scarcity.
- Vocal tendencies.
- Ability as an escape artist.
- Smaller size (some are particularly fine-boned, as well).

Saanen

Compared to other goats, the Saanen is remarkably quiet and laid-back. This, combined with its size and strength, makes it a superb work goat.

Pros:

- Suitability for confinement.
- Adaptability to cool climates.
- Disease resistance.

- Hardiness under proper management.
- Superb disposition; remarkably calm and docile.
- Size.
- Strength.
- Longevity.

Cons:

- Tendency to burrow under fences.
- Susceptibility to sunburn.
- High nutritional requirements.

31. What is the best dog for pulling a cart?

While all dogs can pull a surprising amount of weight, for working on a regular basis, a larger breed will be ideal. The following are dog breeds that excel at hauling things.

Alaskan Malamute

The Alaskan Malamute is a traditional sledding breed. Unlike the Siberian Husky, however, it was bred for strength rather than speed.

Pros:

- Suitability for cold climates.
- Remarkable loyalty.
- Strength.

Cons:

- Unsuitability for homes with other dogs of the same sex.
- Unsuitability for homes with small animals.
- Ability as an escape artist.
- Extensive exercise needs.
- Tendency toward destructive behavior if bored.

- Impressive shedding.
- Poor heat tolerance.
- Tendency to push the limits and vie for dominance.
- Low trainability.

Anatolian Shepherd

The Anatolian Shepherd is typically used as a livestock guard dog, but it has the size and strength to be a useful draft dog, as well.

Pros:

- No slobber.
- Little doggy odor.
- Minimal grooming requirements.
- Surprisingly low food requirements relative to size.
- Moderate exercise needs.
- Adaptability to extremes of both heat and cold.
- Hardiness.
- Few health problems.
- Gentleness with members of his own family, including children.
- Strength.
- Speed.

Cons:

- High risk of lawsuits.
- Size unsuitable for small homes and yards.
- Unsuitability for homes with other dominant dogs.
- Ability as an escape artist.
- Digging tendencies.
- Heavy shedding.
- Night barking.
- Need for an assertive leader.

- Lack of interest in obedience.
- Slow growth.

Bernese Mountain Dog

The Bernese Mountain Dog loves to spend time with his favorite person, and he loves to have a job—a good combination for a farm helper.

Pros:

- Suitability for families with children.
- Excellent cold tolerance.
- Steady, laid-back disposition.
- Moderate energy level.
- Obedience.
- Willingness to work.

Cons:

- Expense.
- Huge size, not a good fit for smaller homes and yards.
- Poor heat tolerance.
- Slobber.
- Shedding.
- Susceptibility to separation anxiety.
- Clumsiness.
- Numerous health problems.
- Short lifespan.

Great Pyrenees

The Great Pyrenees may not be eager to perform whatever he perceives to be pointless activity, but he is certainly big enough and strong enough to pull a cart if sufficiently motivated.

Pros:

- Availability.
- Suitability for families with children, livestock, and most other pets.
- Little doggy odor.
- Low exercise requirements.
- Suitability for the coldest climates.
- Surprisingly low food requirements relative to size.
- Structural soundness.
- Strength.
- Surprising agility.

Cons:

- Unsuitability for small homes and yards.
- Remarkable ability as an escape artist.
- Night barking.
- Slobber.
- Extensive shedding.
- Grooming needs.
- Unsuitability for hot, humid climates, especially if working.
- Resistance to training perceived as pointless.
- Slow growth.
- Short lifespan.

Greater Swiss Mountain Dog

The Greater Swiss Mountain Dog is a competent draft dog for those who are prepared to meet the needs of a giant breed.

Pros:

- Low grooming requirements.
- Gentle but confident disposition.
- Muscularity.
- Sturdy build.

- Surprising athleticism.

Cons:

- High prices.
- Considerable size, not a good fit for some homes.
- Poor tolerance of heat and humidity.
- Slobber.
- Tendency to bark a lot.
- Numerous serious health problems.
- Stubbornness.
- Slow growth and maturity.
- Short lifespan.

Rottweiler

The Rottweiler needs a purpose to be happy—put his strength to use and satisfy his need to work by training him to pull a cart!

Pros:

- Minimal grooming needs.
- Adaptability to cold climates.
- Work ethic.
- Strength.
- Endurance.
- Agility.

Cons:

- Disreputable breeders.
- Legal liabilities.
- Need for supervision around children due to herding tendencies.
- Potential aggression to strangers.
- Unsuitability for homes with other pets.

- Exercise requirements.
- Slobber.
- Heavy shedding.
- Poor heat tolerance.
- Life-threatening health problems.
- Need for an assertive owner.
- Need for owner's constant companionship to avoid behavior problems.
- Need for a job.

Siberian Husky

The Siberian Husky is another sled breed, but lightly built to specialize in speed.

Pros:

- Suitability for cold climates.
- Tidiness.
- Very little doggy odor.
- Relatively low food requirements for size.
- Friendly, agreeable disposition.
- Stamina.

Cons:

- Remarkable ability as an escape artist.
- Unsuitability for homes with cats, other small pets, or small livestock.
- Considerable exercise needs.
- Heavy shedding.
- Strong digging instincts.
- Ability to outthink people.
- Stubbornness.

Chapter 4
Buying Draft Animals

O nce you have determined that draft animals are right for you, and once you know what breed you are most interested in, it's time to purchase and bring home your new farmhands. First, you will need to know how many draft animals you need. Then you will need to find a seller who has what you are looking for.

Deciding What to Buy

32. How do you get started with draft horses?

Assuming that you have already determined that draft animals in general and horses in particular are a good fit for you, first learn as much as you can on the subject. Flip back to the "Helpful Resources" section at the end of this book to increase your knowledge.

Second, you will need to know exactly what to buy:

- **Mare or gelding?** Geldings are more even-tempered and unflappable, but by the same token they can be lazier. Mares are more likely to give their all to whatever is asked of them, but can be more temperamental when in heat. (Stallions are not recommended for beginners.)

- **Age.** Draft horses start slowing down in their teen years, which makes them less suitable for heavy farm work. However, they also have a great deal of experience at this age and can be a great match for a beginner learning the ropes. On the other hand, a younger horse requires more training and may be more of a handful at times, but its greater energy can be helpful when you need to hustle.
- **Appearance.** This may not be important at all for everyday farm work. For those who keep draft horses for promotional purposes, however, a good-looking team is important. This generally necessitates a striking color, usually with uniform markings and often feathering. It is also important that the horses match in size and appearance.
- **Budget.** How much can you spend on a draft team? Know your upper limit and stick to it!

Finally, draft animals need to be working on a regular basis to keep their edge. While you won't be able to purchase a collar until you bring your horse home and measure him, you will want to have most of your equipment and implements on hand right away so that you can start working with your new draft team as soon as possible.

33. Would cows work as oxen?

Cows will work just fine as oxen, even when they are lactating, provided their nutrient needs are met.

However, steers are usually used as oxen due to their greater docility. Cows are much less tractable when in heat or when nursing calves.

34. How many horses will I need for my farm?

Don't underestimate how much work you can do with just one horse. Many small farmers appreciate how easy it is to work with a single horse, especially when learning. Furthermore, it is important to keep your draft animals in work throughout the year so that they don't get "rusty." A horse can plow an acre a day, so if you are only working a few acres, one horse is all you need.

Traditionally, a "one-horse farm" was considered to be about 20 acres. A diversified farm about this size would have just enough work for one horse to do all year long, including plowing, cultivating, haying, and working in the woodlot.

However, a horse is a herd animal and needs to have a companion. Ideally, this will be another horse (a saddle horse will work fine). A donkey or goat can work in a pinch.

The equipment required may be another limiting factor. It can sometimes be easier to find equipment that requires a two-horse team rather than one horse, so be sure to take this into consideration. Plows, mowers, and other implements designed for use with one horse are smaller than those made for teams.

Those entering the world of draft power on a larger scale, such as cash cropping or starting a logging business, will likely need more horses. For many farms larger than 20 acres but still small enough to use animal power, a two-horse team frequently suffices. For logging, four horses are often used in rotation to prevent the animals from becoming exhausted.

Finding Your Draft Team

35. Where are oxen raised?

In North America today, working oxen seem to be most common in the New England states and in adjoining parts of Canada. Some heritage ox breeds are also raised in the Midwest and the Upper South, with a smattering in other parts of the United States.

Even if you can't find someone raising or selling cattle specifically for use as oxen in your area, you can still probably find cattle suitable for the job. This is not ideal for beginners, as you will have to train them yourself, but it will do in a pinch.

36. Where do I buy a draft horse?

These days, there are numerous ways to find draft horses.

An excellent place to start is with the association for your chosen breed. They probably maintain a website with member listings. The Livestock Conservancy also keeps online listings of members raising many draft horse breeds (see the "Helpful Resources" section in the back for more information).

There are also numerous websites listing horses for sale. Some are sites dedicated to selling horses of all types. Others are organizations promoting draft animals, sustainable agriculture, and heritage skills that may allow members to list animals for sale. The latter group of websites is a particularly valuable resource, as these sites can connect you with people in your area with similar interests.

You may be able to adopt a draft horse from a rescue organization. Keep in mind, however, that rescued horses may have health issues or behavior problems due to past mistreatment that can make them unsuitable for work.

Sometimes draft horses are available at auctions, as well. This can be a way to pick up an experienced team, and it will give you a chance to evaluate the horses in person prior to purchase. You may have to search to find auctions in your area.

Making the Purchase

37. What do draft animals cost?

Obviously, this answer depends a great deal on what you are purchasing. Trained animals are more expensive than young, inexperienced weanlings, regardless of species. Flashy animals are typically more expensive than plain-looking ones. Rare breeds generally cost more than common ones.

A surplus Holstein calf can cost less than $300. An older trained steer is more expensive, but still may not cost more than $2,000.

A flashy matched pair of horses can be alarmingly expensive (up to $15,000). However, a sound, trained but plain-looking horse may be only $2,000.

A draft mule foal may not cost more than $1,000. A solid trained pair may be over $12,000.

Donkeys are usually extremely inexpensive, sometimes free, but a purebred American Mammoth Jackstock may cost over $5,000.

38. How should I choose a horse?

One of the most important considerations when it comes to choosing a horse is soundness. If the horse is not sound in limb and wind, it is not suitable for use as a draft animal. Ask to see the horse move for a while, and notice if he moves freely and without pain or discomfort.

Ideally, you will also have a trusted veterinarian examine the horse before you purchase him.

Consider the horse's temperament. Does he take to you readily? Do you like his manner? Watch for any signs of problem behaviors, such as an unwillingness to be handled and groomed. Ask to catch the horse yourself, if possible, and see how both seller and horse respond. Lead him around and pick up his feet. If you can ground drive him (work him in harness but with no load), that's even better.

Starting off with a trained horse is ideal. If this is not possible, he should at least be used to handling and leading.

As you are evaluating the horse, evaluate the seller, too:

- Does he respond to your calls and emails?
- Does he provide pictures and pricing information if asked?
- Is he comfortable with you spending time with the horse before making a decision?

All other factors being equal, choose a horse you love and are drawn to. You will be spending a great deal of time with him for many years to come.

39. Are there things I need to be alert to when I introduce draft animals to the farm?

You should always place new animals in a pen or pasture with substantial (but safe) fencing at first. If you need to introduce them to electric fencing, put up a short length of electrified polytape or something similar in the pen. This way your team will learn to respect temporary fencing in a controlled manner.

They will need fresh water and familiar feed. Before you bring them home, you will want to know what they were eating and how much so that you can make the transition as smooth as possible. Gradually introduce any new feeds over a period of a week.

There are two schools of thought on introducing new animals to animals already residing on your property. The first school of thought is that the new animals could introduce diseases and parasites to your existing animals and should therefore be quarantined for a time. The second school of thought is that the resident animals will have a calming influence on the new animals, making an immediate introduction desirable. If you have purchased only one draft animal, you will certainly want to provide a companion at this time to avoid undue stress. But if you bought a team, it is probably safest to keep them separate from the existing residents for a week or so. It also wouldn't hurt to worm them prior to introduction if they haven't been wormed already.

Be prepared to spend a great deal of time with your new draft team. They need to become used to you for their comfort and yours. Work with them as soon as possible, but start with something simple. Skidding firewood is an ideal task to take on with a new draft team. Learn to read your animals, and allow them to build trust and confidence in you.

Chapter 5
Care and Feeding

D raft animals require a little more care than other types of livestock due to their higher energy output. Keeping your team in top condition requires attention to feeding, grooming, hoof care, and the prevention of sores and galls. Fortunately, as long as you have purchased sound animals, caring for them is not complicated; it just requires extra consideration of their comfort and body condition.

The Basics

40. What routine health care does an equine require, and what does it cost?

Horse care is really not as complicated as it is sometimes made out to be. Like most animals, horses require water and food, most of which should primarily come from the pasture. Draft horses also require basic grooming and hoof care, along with a three-sided shelter that will allow them to escape the weather if they desire.

Compared to other draft animal species, horses require the most inputs to perform draft work. This means high-quality pasture for certain. Most working horses need supplemental feed, too (although not as much as you would expect given their size).

The legs and feet of the Shire and similar breeds are high-maintenance due to size and feathering. The hooves need regular trimming to keep them in peak health, or the weight of the horse will cause them to crack and break down. Also, the feathering must be kept clean and dry to avoid mites and fungus—regular brushing and occasional bathing are in order.

A worst-case scenario per month for routine care for one heavy-breed draft horse breaks down as follows:

- Hay: $160.
- Feed: $60.
- Salt block: $2.
- Hoof trimming and reshoeing: $120.
- Routine veterinary exams: $9.
- Vaccinations: $8.
- Deworming: $13.
- Dental care: $42.
- Shavings (for stall bedding): $115.

The grand total is about $530 in horse care per month.

This estimate assumes that your horse is living in a stall, eating a commercial ration, seeing the farrier once a month, and getting veterinary and dental checkups twice a year (note that the basic veterinary exam is calculated separately from other veterinary costs and that the amount is spread out to arrive at a per-month cost). It does not include whatever your time is worth, nor does it factor in emergency care or mileage charged for farm calls. However, some of these expenses can be reduced (e.g., housing your horse outdoors, letting him work barefoot when conditions permit, feeding him strictly forage plus a mineral supplement in warmer months). Also, prices will vary locally and will fluctuate over time.

Mule care is even simpler, and therefore less expensive. Few domestic animals are as tough as the mule. It rarely gets sick, and it almost never goes lame. Its hooves are exceptionally sturdy and generally don't require shoes unless it is being worked on pavement or very rocky ground. A mule's hoof is very similar to a donkey's hoof and should be trimmed the same way—upright, unlike a horse's hoof.

Even when working, the mule requires very little supplemental feed. A draft mule is estimated to require about a third less feed than an equal-sized working horse.

Donkey care is the simplest of all. Donkeys can thrive with very little feed (less than any other standard draft animal). They require supplemental feed if working hard on a regular basis, but less than a draft horse would. If they work only sporadically, they may not require any feed at all. Either way, donkeys do not require the same level of pasture quality horses do.

However, unlike horses, donkeys are not rain-resistant, and must have shelter from the elements. A three-sided shelter is still sufficient, but it is essential for donkeys.

Also, because donkeys are generally so self-reliant, proper hoof care is sometimes neglected. While donkeys do not need shoes, they still need regular hoof trimming. Again, the hoof is trimmed into a more upright shape than a horse's hoof.

41. Why are draft horses' tails docked?

Historically, draft horses often had their tails docked to prevent inconvenient tangling with the lines, as well as ugly accidents with vehicles and implements. Also, for equipment that required the farmer to sit close behind his team, docking was a way to keep him from getting switched in the face with a horse's tail all day long. These days, it is mostly a cosmetic surgery used on show hitches. Docking is illegal in some states.

Ideally, you will leave your horses with their tails on to give them protection from flies and other insects. For cases when the tail is truly in the way, an alternative to docking is braiding, although it much more time-consuming.

Feed

42. The bigger the horse, the more you need to feed it, correct?

Not necessarily. Heavy horses often need proportionately less feed than light breeds due to their slower metabolisms. However, to compensate for the work they do, they may require some supplemental energy, not to mention vitamins and minerals.

A more significant difference in feeding heavy horses versus feeding light horses is the energy source. Some drafts suffer from equine polysaccharide storage myopathy (EPSM). This condition causes carbohydrates to accumulate in the muscles, leading to tremors. Fortunately, a high-fat, low-starch diet can keep an affected horse in good health.

Providing your draft horse with a diet high in forage is the key to keeping it healthy. Adding a salt lick is another good measure for draft horses that sweat a great deal, as is offering a free-choice mineral supplement. Quality hay may be required seasonally to augment dormant pastures.

How much pasture? In places where grass is lush and rains are frequent, you may only need about one or two acres per horse. In drier climates, a heavy horse may require as much as 10 acres to ensure steady year-round grazing. A good way to figure out how many acres your working horse needs is to find out how many animal units land in your area can typically support. A heavy horse is 2.0 animal units, meaning it requires twice as much space as a 1,000-pound beef cow with a calf. So if it takes five acres to support a cow-calf pair in your region, it will take ten acres to support a heavy-breed horse year-round.

If your horse cannot maintain his body condition on forage alone, due to either hard work or seasonal nutritional shortcomings, then feeding may be required. Commercially prepared products can make feeding draft horses much easier these days, as long as a low-starch feed suitable for easy keepers is selected. These feeds usually contain an ideal balance of vitamins and minerals, so additional supplementation will not be required and may even be harmful.

If your draft horse does require supplemental feed, providing small amounts more often may improve digestion. Draft horse enthusiasts sometimes feed their horses four times a day, sometimes more often.

To check your horse's body condition score (BCS), use this nine-point scale:

1. **Poor.** Obviously extremely emaciated. Bone structures prominent, no fat anywhere on the body. This horse is near death.
2. **Very thin.** Obviously emaciated. Hips, pelvis, and tailhead prominent. Neck, shoulder, and wither bones faintly visible. Some flesh over spine and ribs, but not enough to hide the bones. This horse is in poor health.
3. **Thin.** Neck, withers, and shoulders accentuated. Slight fat cover over ribs, but the bones are still visible. Spine and

tailhead prominent, but individual vertebrae are not visible. Hip joints rounded but still visible.

4. **Moderately thin.** Faint outline of ribs visible. Slight ridge down back. Hip joints not visible. Some fat can be felt around tailhead.

5. **Moderate.** Neck and shoulders blend smoothly into the body. Withers rounded. Back flat and level. Ribs cannot be seen but are easily felt. Tailhead feels spongy.

6. **Moderately fleshy.** Some fat deposits on the sides of the neck, the sides of the withers, and behind the shoulders. Slight crease down back. Spongy fat cover on ribs and tailhead.

7. **Fleshy.** Spongy fat all over body. Crested neck, crease down back, noticeable filling of fat between the ribs.

8. **Fat.** Thick neck. Area along withers filled in with fat. No distinction between shoulder and girth. Ribs hard to feel. Fat deposits on inner thighs. Tailhead very soft. This horse is at risk for health problems.

9. **Extremely fat.** Obviously obese. Bulging fat on neck, shoulders, withers, and tailhead. Patchy fat on ribs. Obvious crease on back. Flanks entirely filled in. Inner thighs may rub together. This horse is at risk for health problems.

Actively working draft horses need adequate fat to meet the demands of their duties. Going into a period of intense work with a BCS between 6 and 7 will give them an energy reserve that will help prevent them from becoming depleted by their work. Once they have been working for a while, they can safely dip as low as a moderate 5 (this weight change is exactly why you will want collar pads).

Similarly, horses kept on pasture year-round should start the winter with a BCS between 6 and 7 so that in spring they will still have a healthy condition score between 5 and 6. This should be no problem for a low-maintenance, easy-keeping breed, as most heavy horses are, although extra monitoring will be required if the horses are performing hard work such as logging throughout the winter.

Both mares and stallions draw heavily on their energy reserves during the breeding season and will need higher body condition scores. A BCS between 6 and 7 is ideal going into the breeding season. By the end of the season, they will probably score between 5 and 6.

A horse that is not actively working should be maintained between 5 and 6.

43. How do you supplement an old horse to bring her weight back up?

This largely depends on the circumstances. You will need to have a rough idea of why she is too thin:

- Has she stopped eating due to painful teeth? In this case, you will need to ask your veterinarian or equine dentist to float (file) her teeth and perform any other necessary dental care.
- Is she fed in a group with other horses? She may no longer be able to hold her own in a pecking order squabble. If this is the problem, she will benefit from being fed alone so that she can get all she needs.
- Is your forage low in nutritional value? Then you will need to offer harvested forages, a balanced mineral supplement, and possibly feed.

Your horse will likely need a diet higher in fat to bring her weight up. For convenience, you may want to source a prepared commercial feed, as developing a balanced horse feed can be tricky. Whatever you feed her, make sure that it is easy to digest.

As for minerals, there are many products available, but some horses seem to do quite well on free-choice kelp meal. Although it is somewhat pricey, it has a balanced mix of nutrients and often gives horses a good "bloom." You can also add ground flax meal to your horse's diet to provide beneficial fatty acids. Follow the supplement manufacturer's directions for the proper dose, but in general a heavy-breed horse can eat around 50 grams daily.

If your older horse is struggling to keep weight on or seems unable to work with comfort, you may need to consider whether or not she is ready to retire. A horse that works particularly hard in its younger years may need to retire in its teens, although this is not a hard-and-fast rule.

Hoof Care

44. Do draft animals need shoes?

In general, draft animals of all species do not need shoes. However, they may need shoes under three specific circumstances:

- To provide traction on slick surfaces, like ice or deep mud.
- To protect their hooves when working on rough surfaces, such as pavement or rocky terrain.
- To compensate for a minor hoof problem (less common in draft horses than saddle horses, but increasingly problematic in horses bred for looks rather than soundness).

45. What type of shoes do draft animals need?

There are two main shoe designs used on draft horses (special shoes to correct hoof problems can take many different forms):

- **Keg shoes.** An open-heel design, sometimes with tungsten carbide welded on for added traction. The standard shape that typically comes to mind when we think of horseshoes.
- **Scotch bottom shoes.** A boxy, straight-toed shape. Traditionally used on soft ground, but now used primarily to accentuate a show horse's stride and action.

Most shoes for draft horses take a great deal of abuse, so they are usually quite thick. In the United States, the shoes are typically ½ inch thick, and 1-1/4 inch wide on the front hooves and 1 inch wide on the back hooves. In places like Scotland where the horses are worked more intensively, 1-1/4-inch-wide shoes are used on the rear hooves, too. The shoes are usually provided with toe clips to reduce the force placed on the nails and clinches.

Most horse shoes made for heavy horses are imported from Europe these days and are typically made from steel. However, shoes can be made of synthetic materials, such as plastic. These are used in cities to protect both the pavement and the hoof. They can also provide beneficial cushioning to horses with a hoof or leg injury.

Pads are usually placed between the hoof and shoe to soften the impact on the horse. These pads also provide some protection from rocks and prevent snow from packing into the hoof. The pad is typically made of either plastic or leather.

When working on sticky clay, horses may benefit from heel calks to give them greater traction. (Calks are projections on the underside of the shoe.)

In winter, draft horses may need to have special screw-in studs put into their shoes when working. The studs give them more traction on snow and ice. Shorter studs are preferred, as long studs can be hard on the joints. These studs must be removed at the end of the day so that the horse doesn't injure itself.

Shoes for mules and donkeys are similar to keg shoes for a horse, but are sized and shaped appropriately.

Oxen working on gravel or concrete can be provided with two-toed shoes. These can be made of steel or iron, but wooden shoes are much easier to fit on and remove for short-term use. Oak is a good, sturdy material for use as an ox shoe.

46. How many people do their own hoof care?

This may be your only choice. Because shoeing draft horses requires special shoes and equipment, many farriers refuse to take on the expense or the burden of acquiring the expertise. Other farriers object to shoeing mules due to their more difficult temperament. Furthermore, shoeing oxen is becoming a lost art, making it a DIY project almost by default.

However, if this seems daunting to you, finding a good farrier who works with heavy horses or mules can be aided by the Internet. Trying visiting the American Association of Professional Farriers website (see the "Helpful Resources" section at the back of this book). If you happen to live near an Amish community, finding a farrier may be easier.

47. How many people do hoof care in stocks versus in the open?

Draft horses are commonly shod in stocks, a restraint very much like the stanchion used for milk cows. Many professional farriers will insist on this measure. Those who do their own shoeing may go either way, depending on their philosophy. That said, there is quite a movement toward shoeing without stocks unless they are necessary to compensate for the home farrier's aching back and joints.

The advantages of shoeing draft animals in stocks include:

- They cannot pull their hooves away from you.
- If the horse is startled, stocks can prevent a dangerous accident to either horse or farrier.
- With proper training, horses can learn that the stocks are a safe place and thus become very relaxed during shoeing.
- Stocks can improve your precision.
- It's easier on your back because you don't have to bend over as far.

Disadvantages of stocks include:

- Animals may be injured if they are not properly restrained and they try to escape.
- Stocks are sometimes used as a substitute for training the horse to accept handling.
- Horses that have to be restrained to have their feet handled are much more prone to panicking in dangerous situations where their feet are caught.

Common Health Problems

48. What kind of cold-weather health problems do people experience with their animals, and what are some precautions?

Warm-season pastures will go dormant in the winter, making hay a necessity and possibly feed, as well, particularly for horses. As previously mentioned in this chapter, keep an eye on your horse's body condition going into the winter. For oxen, feel them over from time to time to make sure they aren't losing too much weight, but aren't getting flabby, either.

All animals need access to fresh water, so if the water tank is freezing you will need to go out and refill it or break the ice. You could also consider a heated waterer or a frost-free nose pump waterer for equines or oxen. The latter never freezes and allows the animals to pump their own water from a shallow water source.

Work horses do not need to be stabled in winter. While many horses will stand out in the snow if given the option, a simple three-sided shelter will enable them to avoid biting winds and freezing rain if they choose. Keeping animals in a barn is more convenient for the owner than the team. If you must keep work horses in a barn, perhaps to make caring for them easier in locations prone to blizzards, do not heat it. Living in a warm barn just makes going outdoors in the cold more taxing. However, the barn absolutely must be dry. Blanket hot, sweaty horses until they have dried off when bringing them indoors.

When logging or performing other work in the winter, check for snow balled up in the hooves. A pad between the hoof and the shoe of the horse will aid in preventing this, but just to be safe it's a good idea to carry a hoof pick in your pocket when working.

Also keep an eye on the wind chill when working in severe cold. Horses working up a sweat pulling logs will benefit from a blanket when taking a break if there is inadequate shelter onsite. A blanket may also be beneficial to animals hauled in a trailer on very cold days.

49. Are occasional galls inevitable or a result of bad collar fit or some other bad decision?

Galls signal a poor-fitting harness. They are caused by recurring friction, particularly over sweaty skin. Once the hair rubs off, there is no protection left and a gall results.

The way a collar fits a horse will change as the horse gains and loses weight from working more or less. If you have an inexperienced horse being put to work for the first time, he will probably lose some weight, which will make his previously well-fitting collar rub, potentially causing a gall. This makes an adjustable collar a great convenience, but adding collar pads will also correct the problem.

Treating galls involves applying medicated ointment. It is even more important, however, to give the horse time to heal. If this is simply not possible, adding a vinyl pad to your horse's collar will help protect the sore.

Chapter 6
Equipment

D raft animal equipment can be hard to find. The good news is that it doesn't have to be expensive. There are several potential sources for finding harnesses and implements, and in some cases you may be able to manufacture your own.

Once you have obtained equipment for working with draft animals, keep it in good repair so that it lasts for your team's lifetime.

Yokes & Harnesses

50. How many collars do you need per horse?

You should only need one properly fitting collar per horse. Then you should take care of it so that it lasts for your horse's entire life. Use collar pads to wick sweat away from the collar. Clean the collar frequently during work and again after work. Use oil on the collar to keep it from drying out and cracking.

Some people do like to have multiple collars, however, either of different types or different sizes to compensate for weight changes in the horse. They feel this offers them more flexibility.

While it never hurts to experiment (or to replace a collar that fits poorly), a collar can last for many years if treated as a valuable investment.

Finally, each horse should have its own properly fitting collar, and collars should not be used interchangeably. A collar that fits one horse well will most likely gall another.

51. Do you use pads to make a collar fit, or do you use pads because they are more comfortable for a horse than a collar alone?

Collar pads are used for a number of reasons:

- To make the collar fit more snugly, thus preventing galls.
- To wick sweat away from the collar, helping it last longer.
- To spread the load more evenly across the collar and thus the horse's shoulders.
- To protect existing sores on a horse that must be worked.

Theoretically, a collar that is well made and fits perfectly requires no padding. However, not all collars are top-notch craftsmanship. But even if you happen to have a well-made collar, it will still fit better at some points in time than others because your horse's weight will change as he works. For this reason, you will likely need to use collar pads.

But no amount of padding will correct a collar that does not fit the horse, so start with the collar size. The most reliable way to ensure a perfect collar fit is to test several collars to find the best match. If this is not possible, you can also measure your horse to put you in the ballpark. There are special tools for this purpose, but you can use a regular cloth tape measure. Measure the horse along the line where the shoulder joins the side of the neck. Hold your measuring tape taut in a straight diagonal line as you take this measurement, not curved around the neck. This number in inches will correspond to the collar size, measured on the inside from top to bottom.

The right collar will fit in the following ways:

- The collar should be snug enough that a man can fit only his fingers (not his whole hand) between the inside of the collar and the side of the horse's neck while pressing the collar firmly toward the horse's shoulders. If your entire hand fits into the collar, it is too big.
- You should be able to run your fingers along the inside of the collar without meeting up with any obstructions (pull the mane free to check this).
- If the collar is drawn very firmly back toward the shoulders (about as hard as you can), there should be about two inches of free space between the horse's throat and the collar, or just enough room to put your fist into, but no more. A short collar will tend to ride up toward the horse's throat and cut off his wind when pulling.
- The collar should lie flat against the shoulder, but free enough to rock slightly if pulled down toward the shoulders. This way it will not interfere with the horse's movement.

A loose collar is far more likely to do harm than a tight collar. A loose collar will rub and gall the horse. A tight collar must be very tight indeed to cause choking.

You will also want to consider your horse's neck shape. Three collar types are available to accommodate a variety of horses:

- **Full face.** For flat, thin necks. Typically used for light horses and mules, but sometimes heavy-breed mares and geldings that are in lighter condition due to hard work.
- **Half sweeney.** For heavier necks with some thickness at the top, but still thicker at the bottom. The most common type

for heavy horses, especially those that are not worked regularly, but will also work for other breeds with a heavier neck such as draft ponies.

- **Full sweeney.** For very thick necks, usually found on stallions but also on chunkier mares.

Once you have found the right collar size, you will still need to fit it to your horse. Lay wet cloths soaked in lukewarm water over the face for about an hour to soften it up a bit. Then put it on the horse while the face of the collar is still damp and work him moderately (don't overdo until the collar is dry and properly fitted). The collar will reshape itself to the horse as he works.

At this point, you are ready to get a pad. Buy a pad two inches larger than the collar size. Leave a gap one or two inches wide so that the horse can breathe freely. If you have padded the collar correctly, it should fit as already described.

52. What are the pros and cons of the different types of bits for mules?

Many of the bits used on draft mules are the same as those used on horses, although ideally they should be shaped differently to accommodate the mule's unique mouth structure (bits shaped for mules will also work on donkeys, by the way). There is a great deal of variety in these bits, with various cheek types, mouthpieces, and materials.

First the cheek types:

- **Full-cheek snaffle.** Offers extra leverage over a regular snaffle. Also prevents you from accidentally pulling the bit out of the mouth.

- **Kimberwick.** Uses mild leverage for more precise communication. Although one of the gentler bits that rely on leverage, it can still be harsh in inexperienced hands.
- **Liverpool.** Has levers to allow for more subtle communication and for more control if an emergency stop is required. Also has multiple slots that allow you to adjust the leverage. Probably the most common bit for draft and driving.
- **Military or elbow.** Adjustable. Shaped to prevent the animal from seizing the bit. Also designed to avoid pinching.
- **Shanked snaffle.** More leverage than a regular snaffle, but less than many other bits. Tends to send a mixed signal. May cause pinching if used incorrectly.
- **Snaffle.** Less prone to upset the animal than a bit with leverage, but also offers less clear communication. Strong draft animals and willful mules can run away with these, which is why a bit with some leverage is frequently used for draft purposes.

Next the mouthpieces:

- **Arch mouth.** Gives more clearance for the tongue, which may be more comfortable for some animals. However, it does increase the pressure on the bars (toothless parts of the jaw where the bit sits).
- **French link.** A jointed mouthpiece with two joints. Milder action than a single joint.
- **Simple jointed.** Acts on the tongue and bars of the mouth with a nutcracker action.
- **Straight bar.** Usually very mild, but can cause discomfort in animals with growing or painful teeth.
- **Twisted wire.** Can be jointed or unjointed. Allows for strong control if necessary. Can be extremely harsh, causing dramatic reactions in animals that are not used to it. Also can

cause sores in the mouth if a wire end gets loose. Typically used for starting mules or correcting mules with bad habits.

Then there are the materials:

- **Brass.** Encourages salivation, which is necessary for good bit lubrication and subsequently the animal's comfort.
- **Chrome-plated.** Tends to peel after a time, which can cut the mouth.
- **Rubber.** One of the mildest materials, but some animals will not salivate with it.
- **Steel.** Cheap and durable. Can have sharp edges if poorly made.
- **Sweet iron.** Not as popular because it rusts, which is cosmetically unappealing. Equines accept it readily, however, because they seem to like the taste.

So-called "mule bits" can be extremely harsh in the wrong hands (even well-meaning but inexperienced hands), as they often have teeth and sharp edges. An experienced mule trainer can use a mule bit with finesse to work with a problem mule or to convince a young mule not to ignore the bit (although other mule trainers refuse to have anything to do with a "mule bit"). Unless you have a light touch on the reins, you probably don't want to risk using a mule bit.

When you purchase your mule, it's a good idea to find out from the seller what bit the mule is used to and start out with that. If this is not an option, you will need to resort to trial and error. Choose several bits and use them with your mule in the safety of a round pen to see how he responds to each.

Also note that the width of the bit is important, as a bit that is too big or too small will pinch the mule's lips and put him in a bad mood. A simple way to measure a mule for a bit is to knot a short length of rope at one end and then insert the rope into the mouth across the bars with the knot against the cheek. Use your thumb and forefinger to mark where the unknotted end of the rope comes out of the mule's mouth, remove the rope, and measure between the knot and your fingers. This measurement in inches corresponds to the bit size your mule will need.

53. What is the ideal harness for a goat?

Goat carting has attracted enough fans to make finding equipment fairly simple. Just be sure to use equipment designed specifically for goats. Pony carts are too heavy for goats, and they tend to apply potentially damaging pressure to the goat's spine. Likewise, you will want to buy a harness made for goats, rather than for dogs, as a dog harness does not have all the straps and safety features necessary for goat carting. It can also be hard to get onto a horned goat.

Make sure the harness you select is a goat driving, pulling, or work harness, depending on your needs. You may see other goat harnesses, which will not work for this purpose. For instance, you may see a marking harness. This is designed to be fitted with a crayon and placed on a buck to mark the does he has bred. It is not suitable for draft work.

Also, never use a collar for pulling with a goat, as it could very easily crush the goat's windpipe.

Harnesses you might be interested in include:

- **Ground driving harness.** This is an inexpensive simplified harness for training goats to respond to the driving commands, not for pulling a load.
- **Multipurpose/cart harness.** This is a complicated and expensive harness, but it is quite versatile and very safe. It includes a breeching, or butt strap, which is essential for

braking wheeled vehicles. It uses loops to balance the cart shafts.

- **Wagon harness.** Somewhat like the cart harness, but without the loops for the shafts. Only safe for stable vehicles like sleds and four-wheeled wagons.
- **Work harness.** This simple harness is made for plowing and brush work (the caprine equivalent of logging). It does not include the breeching. Therefore, for safety, it should not be used with wheeled vehicles.

A good harness should be durable and well padded.

54. What is the best dog harness for cart pulling?

You will want to get a harness made specifically for this purpose. Some harnesses are designed to discourage a dog from pulling on the leash, and this will defeat the purpose. Carting, sledding, and other draft-type harnesses for dogs usually have comfortable padding to help your pooch pull with ease. A 1"-wide webbing will also help distribute the load more evenly.

If you are planning to work on the road, it's a good idea to get a harness with reflective tape for greater visibility.

Once you have selected a suitable type of harness from your favorite pet supply store, make sure you follow the manufacturer's directions for measuring the fit. You will likely need to know the diameter of your dog's neck and chest girth (measured just behind the elbows).

Vehicles & Implements

55. What draft-powered options are available for plowing?

You may be surprised at the variety of animal-powered plows that exist:

- **Georgia stock plow.** Comes with interchangeable parts to allow for working crops of different types and sizes.
- **Lister (middlebreaker).** Throws soil up each way, making ridges.
- **Moldboard plow.** The classic walk-behind plow that you probably think of immediately.
- **New ground plow.** Mostly for breaking roots.
- **Snow plow.** For winter work.
- **Sulky plow.** Includes a seat for the operator.
- **Swivel plow.** Made to throw furrows one way as the operator walks back and forth in rows.
- **Turning plow (breaking plow).** Exactly what the name says, a plow for turning over soil.

56. Where are the implements for no-till systems using a draft animal?

One thing you will need is an animal-drawn crop roller or roller-crimper. This knocks down existing ground cover without using chemicals and leaves it in a mat. This mat hinders weed growth and will slowly decompose as the season progresses, adding nutrients to the soil. As long as your cover crop grew well, this method is shockingly effective.

You will also need a no-till drill for planting. You can use a smaller drill designed for use with a tractor, but many of these are PTO-driven, so you will also need a handy device called a PTO forecart if you go this route. Although not common or inexpensive, there is also a no-till drill made for use with ATVs that could be adapted to your purpose.

The PTO forecart is commonly used by those who seriously farm with draft animals. It will increase the versatility of your team, and not just in no-till, because you can use it to operate many PTO implements by converting the forward motion of your team into power. Some even come with battery-powered hydraulics. (Keep in mind that PTO forecarts work better with faster draft animals like horses, not so much with oxen.)

All of these items can be found online through a simple search. Manufacturers are increasingly stepping up to the plate and meeting the demand for draft animal equipment. (Also be sure to check the helpful resources in the back of this book for links that will lead you to more suppliers and information.)

57. Does anyone use a cultivator with oxen?

Traditionally, cultivation was often done with horses and mules because of their agility and control, a must for such a precise application. However, cultivation can be done with oxen, as well. In fact, for small farms, a single ox can be quite effective for cultivation.

The key is proper training. To start out, you will need a helper to lead the ox and keep him in the furrows while you operate the cultivator and give vocal commands. As your ox becomes used to this routine, have your helper increase his distance from the ox, walking several rows to the left so that the ox learns to rely on your commands.

58. Where should I look for modern covered horse-, donkey-, and mule-drawn wagons and carts?

Try one of these places:

- Local farm auctions.
- Online antique farm equipment dealers.
- Carriage manufacturer websites.
- Amish communities.

If all else fails and you are handy with tools, you could try making one yourself. Plans abound, and kits are also available from online sellers.

59. What equipment is necessary for logging with horses?

Horse-drawn logging equipment is really not that complicated.

The harness for a logging horse is different than the harness for a draft horse. For logging, a New England D-ring harness is commonly used because it keeps the angle of the trace ideal while reducing the amount of jouncing that will be placed on the horse's collar.

Then you will need a collar for the horse.

A choker chain is used to skid the logs. You will also need another chain with a slot hook.

You will need a cant hook for turning over the logs when loading them. A cant hook is a wooden pole with a hinged, hooked iron bar on the end. You might also appreciate the similar peavey, which has a spike at the tip of the pole.

Various logging arches are used to transport wood out of the forest. An arch is a simple metal frame with wheels that makes it easier for the horse to pull the logs.

And finally, you will need your chainsaw, ax, and the appropriate safety gear.

There are other things you may want to pick up over time, but this is sufficient for a start.

60. What kind of wood is used to make ox yokes?

Many different woods are suitable for making yokes. Traditionally, the sturdiest wood available locally was used for the beam, or the horizontal piece. Common woods used include:

- Ash.
- Basswood.
- Beech.
- Birch.
- Cherry.
- Elm.
- Locust.
- Maple.
- Oak.

The wood for the ox bows, or the part underneath the ox's neck, is more specific. The bows can be made of metal, but wooden bows are usually made of something especially durable, often hickory.

61. How do you make a harness?

Harness-making is an art requiring patience and skill to learn. It is by no means something you can master in a day, and it's not really a subject this book can fully explain.

If you happen to have access to a harness-maker who would be willing to mentor you, you're in luck.

Another option is to find a harness manufacturer who sells harness-making supplies and buy individual parts so that you can put the harness together yourself.

You could also learn by restoring an old harness, which will give you hands-on experience with how the whole thing is put together.

Be sure to check the helpful resources at the back of this book—you'll find some old public domain books with a great deal of information on this subject.

62. How do you wash fluffy collar pads?

Fluffy collar pads are quite easy to care for, whether they are deer hair or fake fur:

1. Brush off all the horse hair.
2. Run them through the washing machine, as many times as necessary to get them clean.
3. Run them through the normal dryer cycle (add a few tennis balls with fake fur pads to fluff them up).

If for any reason machine washing is not an option, this works in a pinch:

1. Allow the pads to air dry.
2. Brush them off with a medium-stiff horse brush to remove debris.

Chapter 7
Working with Draft Animals

In some ways, working with draft animals is not as simple as working with tractors and other machines. With a well-maintained tractor, you can just about check the fuel, start the ignition, and go. Draft animals, however, have personalities that must be taken into consideration.

An important step is to build a bond with your animals. You will need to earn their trust and learn to read their body language.

There are also safety considerations. Proper training, conditioning, and harnessing are necessary to prevent serious accidents. Also, for the health of your team, you will need to accommodate their needs and comfort, and learn to make adjustments for different working conditions.

63. Do working animals such as draft horses and sled dogs work better together if they're friends?

Draft team compatibility is certainly something to be considered. A matched team is one with animals that are similar in size and appearance. However, disposition is also important.

Good draft animals aren't unduly prone to kicking or biting each other, although no animal relationship will be perfect at all times.

Allowing your team members to be pasture mates is a good idea, as it will help them establish a pecking order and build rapport. If you bought your draft animals separately, you should give them time to get acquainted with each other. You will likely also benefit from watching their interactions so that you have a feel for their personalities and leadership abilities.

Keep in mind, though, that it is even more important that your draft animals respect you as their ultimate leader. If they are sidetracked from their work by squabbling, you are justified in reprimanding them, because they should be focused on you rather than on the other animals.

64. Should I be able to load my horses together in full harness?

This depends on the horses and on the trailer. To do this, you will need ample room in the trailer. Just scope it out and use your common sense.

65. How do you work with a donkey's temperament?

This can certainly be a challenge. If a horse is somewhat like a dog in temperament, then a donkey is more like a cat. Attempts at coercion will backfire. Donkeys can also be extremely wary, especially when young. Be prepared to earn their trust and to exercise a great deal of patience when dealing with potentially frightening situations. Also keep in mind that they will never allow themselves to be overworked or placed in danger. For most beginners, starting with a trained donkey is the best bet. Even at that, donkeys are reluctant to do just about anything that doesn't make sense to them.

The first thing to do is to earn your donkey's trust, even if he has previously been trained. This should be done before the harness is ever in place. It is not so much a procedure as a process. It involves forming a solid bond with your donkey throughout your daily routine. Building trust requires attention to simple things:

- Always stay calm around your donkey, no matter what happens; take a break and go somewhere else if you can't keep your cool.
- Speak to him in a quiet tone.
- Establish a donkey care routine and stick with it every day. Be consistent.
- If you are giving him hay or feed, bring it to him, and only just as much as he needs in one meal so that he learns that you are the provider in his life.
- Pet, handle, and groom him frequently. Find his favorite spot to be touched and rub it often.
- Never grab at him or make any other abrupt movements. In particular, never grab his feet.
- Give him time to inspect any and all unfamiliar objects, including tack, tools, grooming supplies, etc.

If you are dealing with a donkey that has previously been mistreated, let him make the first move and decide to approach you himself. (You can aid this process by setting up a chair in the pasture and getting comfortable with a book for the afternoon.)

A donkey that refuses to trust you regardless of your best efforts should be examined by a veterinarian, as he could be in pain, or he might be blind or deaf. Also note that jacks are frequently hard to handle; a gelding is strongly recommended for your own safety.

As you work with your donkey, remember that he will always be keeping an eye on you to see if you really mean what you say. Again, be consistent. Draft work will become an extension of the bonding process you have already gone through. Always make his efforts fun and worth his while. You will have to be on your toes so that you don't miss an opportunity to reward him with praise or a friendly pat when he does right.

However, you may also need to carry a whip to correct him when he is willful. The whip can be a very humane training aid when used properly. It is used to tap the donkey as a mild correction, never to hit him. If you give your donkey a command to go forward, for instance, and he doesn't budge, tap the whip on his hindquarters, near the back legs, to convince him that you mean what you say.

66. Can the information on draft goats translate directly to sheep?

Working with draft sheep is similar in many ways to working with draft goats. For example, the same harnesses can be used. However, sheep are more delicate and cannot pull as much weight. Introduce a cart without any weight at all at first, and never add more weight than they can comfortably pull without straining.

The easiest way to train a sheep to pull a cart is to teach it to be led with a halter, and then add a cart with the aid of some treats. Sheep have a harder time learning commands than goats, so you will need to lead them when they are working.

Finally, watch out for overheating in wool sheep.

Hitching Up

67. Why are oxen yoked together?

Oxen are yoked to increase their pulling power, although, for a small farm, a single ox can still be quite useful. Oxen are worked with yokes rather than harnesses partly because the yoke makes them walk at the same pace and partly because pushing with the head, neck, and shoulders is a natural movement for bovines, commonly used to establish pecking order.

68. How many oxen are in a span?

Two.

69. Where should I place the smaller ox in a yoked pair?

Place the smaller ox on the near (left) side, closest to you. This will enable you to easily see both the smaller ox and the larger ox.

Ideally, however, you will choose similarly sized oxen so that they will work comfortably together. If you notice they are growing at different rates, you might want to offer some supplemental feed to the smaller ox to encourage it to catch up a bit. A slight height difference is to be expected, of course, but you don't want to work with severely mismatched oxen. It's fine for training, but in the field or woodlot they will be too uncomfortable to work together efficiently.

70. What are the proper names for the right and left horse?

The horse on the team's left side is the near or nigh horse. The horse on the team's right side is the off or far horse.

71. How do you attach a goat to a cart?

First you will want to train your goat to lead with a collar so he is easy to handle. Once he is comfortable with this, add the halter. Just let him sniff it over and then wear it (with supervision) to get him used to the idea. Then you can practice leading him with the halter. Be sure to be liberal with the praise and pats—goats love to be the center of attention. Also, keep your training sessions brief so that your goat is engaged. Many short sessions are far more effective than a few lengthy ones.

Next, start to add the basic commands, guiding the goat with the lead for this step. The most common commands are:

- Forward.
- Whoa.
- Haw (left).
- Gee (right).
- Back.

However, you can use any words you want to convey these concepts.

As your goat learns to respond to the commands, gradually move back toward his shoulder and ask him to respond to the commands while you are in this position. Then move behind him so you are actually driving him.

Next add the harness (again, let him sniff it first) and walk your goat around in it for a while. Once the goat is used to wearing the harness, have him practice the basic commands in harness.

Once your goat obeys reliably to these commands while wearing a harness, you are ready to add an empty cart (no weight yet). First let him sniff it over, and then get him used to walking with you on a leash while you pull the cart so that he can see and hear it move. Once he is comfortable with the cart, hitch him to it. Ask the goat to move forward. Walk with him and speak encouragingly to assure him that everything is safe. Don't try anything fancy just yet.

If your goat is relaxed and upbeat about this stage of progress, you can start to add weight. However, go slow and give him time to build muscle, just like a human athlete. Start by adding half your goat's weight to the cart and letting him haul it around for a few days until it seems effortless to him. Then gradually add more and more weight over time until he is pulling at his full capacity (females can pull their own weight, males twice their own weight).

At this point, further training will focus on introducing the goat to a wide variety of situations, all in a safe, controlled, and positive way. Gradually add distractions and new environments until you and your goat are confident working together.

Now, a word on how you get the harness on a goat. First off, always brush your goat before harnessing him. The attention will help him associate work with good things, and the grooming will remove any debris caught in his hair that could cause irritation under a harness.

Next, to put on the harness tighten the cinch strap first; it goes around the goat, behind the elbows. Then comes the breast strap across the chest, then the breeching around the hindquarters. The reins go through the loops on the back pad. The cart shafts go through the shaft loops on the sides of the harness. The exact configuration depends on the harness, so be sure to get a picture or instructions from your harness manufacturer.

Off to Work

72. How many acres can a farmer plow with a mule in one day?

Estimates vary, but generally one mule can plow one acre per day working solo.

73. In what depth of snow can horses log?

A lot depends on your horses' energy and how well-packed the snow is. Loose, powdery snow is tiring to a team, while a well-packed trail should present no problem.

Many heavy horses can log in snow as deep as two feet. The main thing is to monitor your team and notice if they are floundering or breathing heavily. Many loggers bring along four horses in snowy weather so that each team can take a rest periodically while the work continues.

To make working in snow safer and easier, consider these tips:

- Keep your horses in top physical condition.
- Use calks on your horses' shoes to give them traction.
- Give the horses frequent opportunities to catch their breath when breaking a snowy trail.
- Bring along a pry bar to free logs that have frozen to the ground.
- Use a sledge instead of a wheeled arch to extract the logs.

If the snow is just too deep, your best bet is to find another chore to tackle, unless you have the equipment to clear the trails.

74. How steep can horses skid?

Horses can skid steeper than you would think, and certainly far steeper than any tractor can climb. If you can walk it, a horse can log it.

The key is to keep the log from outrunning the horses. You may need to use a longer chain, perhaps as long as 20 feet, over very steep portions of a trail to put more distance between the log and the team. Also, cut the logs longer to increase their surface area and create more friction, thus slowing the descent.

Tackling the hill in a series of switchbacks will help considerably. In fact, you can design your whole trail system through the woods this way. For extra safety, cut poles to span gaps between tree trunks and form a rail on the downhill side of the slope. These poles will catch the logs and prevent them from rolling down.

However, when skidding on a steep slope, you must have confidence in your team. If you have any doubts, your safest option is to use a peavey to roll the logs down the hill to a point where you feel you can safely extract them.

75. What skid distance is possible?

This depends a great deal on what you are trying to accomplish and what equipment you have available. A horse team can work briskly enough to be quite efficient ground skidding for a distance of 300 feet or so. Add a wheeled arch to the equation, and the team may be efficient at distances up to as much as 1,500 feet.

At some point beyond this, a tractor would probably have an advantage due to its greater speed and indefatigability. Fatigue is the greatest limiting factor on how far animals can skid logs.

Chapter 8
Training Tips

Ideally, if you are an absolute beginner, you will start out with a trained team. However, because draft animals and the associated know-how are not so common, you may have little choice but to train your own draft animals.

A few major principles apply no matter what species you are working with:

- Be consistent. Animals develop trust more quickly when they see humans acting predictably. (This is one way in which having a routine can help.)
- Insist on respect at all times, including when you are not actively working your team.
- Start slowly, adding only one new concept, distraction, or piece of equipment at a time, and not progressing until your pupil is relaxed and comfortable.
- Always reward a job well done. The reward should include a word of praise, a friendly pat, and a release of pressure (e.g., loosening up on the lines, removing the goad, stepping back to give the animal more space, etc.).

Training Oxen

76. How are oxen trained?

Oxen begin preliminary lessons in draft work while still calves. Obviously, they don't pull loads at this young age, but they can learn to accept handling and leading on a halter. Pat them, groom them, and take them for walks. Get them used to being touched from behind. Repetition is a must when training oxen, but do keep the training sessions brief so that they don't become bored.

When they are about 6 to 12 months old, oxen can be taught the basic commands ("get up" for forward, "gee" for right, "haw" for left, and "whoa" to stop). At first, do this while leading them. You will need a lightweight ox goad (a thin stick works) to train these commands, using the goad for guidance and later as a reprimand for disobedience. When training "whoa," for instance, tap (don't hit) the oxen on the nose with the goad to teach them to stop. For "get up," tap them on the rump. As they become reliable with the four basic commands, you can introduce more advanced cues, such as "easy" for slow down.

Next fit them with a calf yoke. Introducing the yoke at various times throughout the day will help prevent the oxen from associating it with something unpleasant (this works with halter training, too). Once they accept the yoke, start adding the commands one at a time until they respond reliably while wearing the yoke.

As soon as this task is complete, start your oxen on real work, but keep it light at first. Oxen have to be trained physically just as much as mentally. Give them light logs of firewood diameter to pull for short distances. Increase the difficulty of their work little by little as they demonstrate their understanding and as they become strong enough to pull more weight without straining. (Do not expect them to pull at their full capacity until they are physically mature.)

77. Is yoking a young ox with an old one to train the younger ox a myth or superstition?

Actually, this training practice is not uncommon and can be used to accustom younger oxen to verbal commands. The biggest challenge in training with this method comes from differences in size between the two oxen. A yoke with bows of different sizes will be required to accommodate them, and the oxen should not be expected to pull any great weight.

78. How do I teach them to always stop?

First off, respect is everything with oxen. If you want them to always stop, they must always regard you as the herd leader, even when not in the yoke. Most oxen will test your dominance from time to time. If they shove their heads into you, a flat-handed smack on the nose is in order, never in anger or as a punishment, but to make it perfectly clear that such behavior is unacceptable. If they lower their heads at you in a threatening way, walk toward them until they yield to the pressure and turn to the side. With a really stubborn team, become the sole provider of food for a time. (This means you can't leave hay sitting out, so be sure they get as much as they need as often as they need.)

Second, you need to give them a fair chance to learn the command "whoa." Start without a yoke, just leading them with a halter (preferably one at a time at first, but eventually in pairs). Start them and stop them repeatedly, using a tap on the nose with the goad to give them the idea that "whoa" means stop. When they obey, reward them by removing the goad pressure and by praising them and stroking them.

Finally, once your oxen understand what "whoa" means, you must not take no for an answer. Keep using the goad for discipline as needed if your team disobeys.

79. How do you hitch a horse double for the first time?

Before you try this, make sure each horse is used to working with you singly in a relaxed manner, both with a load and without.

Start by ground driving the horses in a round pen without a load. Horses are herd animals, so usually they will take to this without much trouble. If they tend to want to swing away from each other, clip their harnesses together at the breeching, and keep them moving forward. If one horse tries to forge ahead, use gentle pressure on the lines to encourage him to relax and work with the other horse. When the faster horse yields, be sure to release the pressure immediately as a reward.

As soon as your horses are calm and comfortable, add a light log or tire for them to pull. Start out in the round pen again, but as they become more reliable you can take them out for practice in a safe real-world setting with few distractions.

As their confidence and yours increase, you can gradually transition them to real working situations, such as pulling a cart. Just make one change at a time and give your team as long as they need to become fully comfortable before adding something new. This includes new skills, new objects to pull, new distractions, and new environments to work in.

Many experienced horsemen advise never leading horses that are pulling an empty cart, however. While this is a great training step for some animals, horses are easily frightened by the noise, which diminishes when the cart is loaded. When adding the cart for the first time, you will want to have some weight in it to reduce the noise. You can also ease the tension of this step by having an assistant pull the cart through the round pen so that you can introduce your horses to the sight and sound before hitching them up to it.

80. How do you train a draft horse to stand patiently while working in the woods?

This tends to be more problematic with young, energetic horses, so one good thing to do is to make sure the horse has enough work. If he is busy, he will be glad to take a rest soon enough (just be sure to rest him before he's completely worn out). Let him rest long enough to catch his breath, but don't keep him standing around waiting, either.

If your horse still starts moving without your permission, gently guide him back to his place with line pressure and command him to "stand" (or whatever word you use) again. As soon as he is quietly in his place, release the pressure.

A horse that is having trouble grasping the concept may benefit from some work in the round pen. Tell him to stand and start introducing mild distractions, gradually working up to more severe distractions. If at any time he moves, make him back up to his proper position and try again. Many horses do not appreciate being made to back up for any considerable distance, so this will be a good disincentive.

Training Mules, Donkeys, and Others

81. How is fine-tuning a mule's training different than fine-tuning a horse's training?

The short answer is that it's much, much harder. Mules are smart, and they can easily become set in their ways. If they have gotten by with something in the past, they will continue to try it out.

Mules aren't exactly stubborn—they're just super independent, and they have an exceptional ability to spot a person who isn't really in control, as previously mentioned. Training mules for draft work is extremely challenging and time-consuming. Mistakes have long-term ramifications, and bad habits are extraordinarily difficult to weed out. Most beginners probably will not want to tackle this project when they are first learning to work with draft animals.

Even a well-trained mule will disobey if it feels the need, and it will insist on taking time to look over any and all dubious situations before proceeding. This is precisely due to its self-preservation instinct. Beneficial though this instinct may be in many situations, not everyone can (or wants to) handle mule nature. Horses are far less independent.

This explains why beginners are advised not to train their own mule team the first time out. It is much safer and much less frustrating to start with a well-trained team.

82. How do you train a donkey to pull a wagon?

Trust is a huge factor when training donkeys to do pretty much anything, so you will need to start off with an excellent relationship. Assuming your donkey is already trained to accept handling and being led on a halter, you should be ready to begin.

Start by putting the harness on the donkey. This should actually be much easier than introducing a harness to a horse, because donkeys are not prone to panic. Just be sure to lavish him with praise and petting.

Once your donkey gets over his disgust, you can introduce ground driving in a safe, enclosed area such as a round pen. Teach him the basic commands while leading him at first, but gradually move into a position behind him.

Next introduce the cart. This can be quite easy if you pull the cart into the pasture where the donkey can sniff it over. Once he accepts the empty cart, hitch him to it and practice leading him around. As this becomes second nature, you can start driving him with the cart. In no time, you should be ready to add some weight to the cart.

Remember, donkeys respond very well to positive reinforcement. Always praise and pat your donkey lavishly for a job well done.

83. Do donkeys respond to controlling movement the way horses do?

Horses, being prey animals, tend to be quick to respond to a person's approach. If you pressure their "flight zone" by walking toward them, their natural instinct (modified by personality and training, of course) is to yield and put more distance between you and them. Therefore, this type of "controlling movement" is frequently used in horse training, with pressure being applied as a cue or form of discipline and pressure being removed as a reward.

Donkeys operate quite differently than horses. They tend to react less in fear and act more independently. They also get bored far more easily. While donkeys, also being prey animals, do respond to pressure to some degree, a better way to train your donkey is to start by building trust and using positive reinforcement. Spend time with him, creating pleasant experiences on a daily basis. Then show him what you want him to do and reward his efforts.

84. How can I train my dog to pull a cart?

The main steps are as follows:

1. Accustom the dog to the sight, sound, and smell of both cart and harness.
2. Train your dog to accept wearing the harness.

3. Hitch your dog to the cart and reward him, but without moving the cart.
4. Guide your dog on a leash while he pulls the empty cart.
5. Use leash pressure and rewards to train your dog to respond to the various commands for starting, stopping, and turning.
6. Let your dog pull the cart with a very light weight in it.
7. Gradually add weight over time.

How fast you proceed will depend on your dog's temperament. A confident dog will adapt to the cart quickly, but may need more discipline as he tests you to see if obeying the commands is a must. A dog that is afraid of the cart should be introduced very slowly, and care must be taken that every experience with it is positive (treats help).

Chapter 9
Raising Your Own Draft Animals

Raising your own draft animals requires a considerable commitment. You must be willing to learn a great deal about basic livestock genetics and about the care of breeding animals.

That said, raising your own draft animals can not only be economical in some cases, it can also add a new stream of income to your farming enterprise.

Breeding Draft Animals

85. Is breeding my own draft animals a reasonable course?

For the absolute beginner, breeding your own draft animals is probably not what you want to do because of the great amount of work involved.

You will first want to make sure that draft animals work well on your farm. You will want to be sure that you like your chosen breed. Then you will want to develop extensive knowledge of draft animals:

- How a good working animal is built.

- How to choose the right breeding stock.
- What genetic problems lurk in your chosen breed.
- How to care for breeding animals.
- How to assist with a birth, if necessary.
- How to train young draft animals.

Next you will want to set clear objectives. You will want to know exactly how your ideal draft animal measures up in several key ways:

- Temperament.
- Conformation.
- Health.

Then you will need a plan to reach your objectives. This includes choosing a breeding system. Will your animals be purebred or crossbred? How closely will they be related? Mating genetically similar animals will result in greater consistency but less hybrid vigor; mating genetically dissimilar animals will boost hybrid vigor but produce less consistent results.

Once you know what you want to achieve and how you want to achieve it, you will be ready to select breeding stock. You cannot afford to compromise on the quality of your breeding stock, which means you may have to pay more to get what you want. Selecting inferior breeding animals is a sure way to produce inferior offspring. It is better to settle for fewer animals but buy really good ones.

Along the way, you will need to keep very clear and detailed records on every decision you make.

You will also want to have a plan for keeping a large intact male animal safely, unless you intend to use artificial insemination, take your mare to a stud, or rent a local bull.

Breeding mules in particular creates a difficult scenario. Horses and donkeys typically will not breed unless they have been raised with members of the other species right from the start.

There is one exception to the recommendation against breeding your own draft animals as a way to get started. That is the case of the family milk cow. If you are already keeping a milk cow, you are already raising calves, presumably for beef. In this case, it makes sense to try to save a sturdy, well-built calf to train as a draft ox.

Also, once you have gained some experience with draft animals, breeding your own will likely become an increasingly viable option. It will save you the trouble of hunting high and low for suitable animals, and it can become a complementary stream of income, as well.

86. Are mules sterile?

Most mules are sterile due to genetic differences between their donkey and horse parents. However, the occasional molly mule can breed and give birth, a phenomenon that scientists still can't explain.

87. Can I breed an EPSM horse?

Equine polysaccharide storage myopathy (EPSM) is a heritable disease common in draft breeds. It causes abnormal sugar levels to build up in the muscles. A horse with EPSM may appear normal when standing still, but when asked to move may suddenly "tie up" or become stiff and sore.

While EPSM is a genetic condition, there is some question as to whether we have inadvertently created the disease in otherwise healthy horses by feeding diets with far too much starch and sugar. After all, about two thirds of all heavy horses show symptoms of EPSM. What to do about EPSM then comes down to whether genes or diet is the primary cause. If the problem is bad genetics, then the solution would be to avoid breeding horses with EPSM. If the problem is primarily dietary, perhaps we need to rethink the way we feed draft horses.

With this in mind, what some veterinarians recommend is putting the horse on a high-fat, low-starch diet and seeing how it responds. If it thrives, go ahead and breed it. If it fails to respond to dietary adjustment, then assume something isn't right and do not breed the horse.

Raising a Draft Prospect

88. What should I look for in a calf that will make a good ox?

You will want to evaluate your calves for the following characteristics:

- A tractable but active disposition.
- Good health.
- Soundness, especially in the feet and legs.
- Good muscling.

Also, horns are usually a necessity to hold the yoke in place.

When evaluating conformation as it relates to soundness, look for the following:

- A straight back.
- All four hooves pointing straight forward.
- High heels with the hairline well off the ground.

If you are going to put together a team, you want your oxen to grow at about the same rate, so choose calves that are the same age and about the same size. Some people also prefer their oxen to match in color and overall appearance.

89. What is the castration period for oxen?

Part of this decision will come down to how you want to deal with the animal discomfort factor, and part of it will depend on the breed you have. Many steers are castrated shortly after birth to reduce the pain of the operation. For steers that are destined to become work oxen, however, castration is usually performed later to take advantage of the higher testosterone levels that will ensure strength and good growth.

In general, oxen are frequently castrated at around six months of age. Fast-growing breeds can be castrated as early as one month of age to reduce their discomfort, provided they have good muscling by that time. Big, fast-growing breeds destined for competitive pulling will develop more strength if they are left intact until a year old.

Chapter 10
Because You Always Wondered

H ave you ever wondered why we say *oxen*, not *oxes*? Are you curious about what the Native Americans used for draft purposes? Do you contemplate why draft horses have feathers? Now you will have the answers.

History

90. Why *oxen*, not *oxes*?

As has been repeatedly pointed out on the Internet, the plural of *box* is *boxes*, but the plural of *ox* is *oxen*. This is because *ox* and *oxen* are relics of Old English. In Old English, most plurals were formed by adding *–en* rather than *–s*. Another example is *children* instead of *childs*.

91. What is the history of the draft animal?

Draft animals have been used across the entire world since the most ancient times. As long as man has desired to transport heavy loads, he has also desired to have animals assist him.

The ox was probably the first draft animal due to its great strength and steady disposition (horses and mules were typically ridden in the most ancient days). Oxen originally pulled sledges, but the wheel was invented about the time the ancient Mesopotamian civilization of Sumer was founded. Once the wheel came into being, it was not long before the ox cart was developed. The dominance of oxen as draft animals continued into medieval times.

However, during the Crusades, a new horse breed came into prominence. This was the Great Horse, a large, sturdy animal used to carry knights in shining (and extremely bulky) armor. After the Crusades ended and battles with firearms and cannons became the norm, such horses were adopted as powerful draft animals to pull plows, coaches, and heavy artillery. Horses were faster than oxen, which made them preferable in the eyes of many farmers, although the use of oxen continued where soils were particularly heavy.

In the early days of American settlement, people arrived from many different parts of Europe, often bringing their native breeds of horses and cattle with them. As the settlers mingled and adapted to their new homes, so did their livestock. Everywhere people farmed there were small populations of genetically distinct livestock, especially adapted to their local conditions. (These populations are now called landraces.) However, some British breeds remained in use in a pure state. Thus, in the days after the American Revolution, the American-made Morgan horse and Lineback ox were common choices for plowing purposes, but so was the British Devon ox.

About this time, George Washington, seeing a largely undeveloped country before him, realized that a sturdy animal would become the basis of agriculture and transportation for years to come. Washington concluded that a large type of mule was needed. King Charles III of Spain sent Washington a big jack named Royal Gift, and this was put to stud along with a Maltese jack from Lafayette. Soon afterward, the cotton gin was invented, and the big draft mules of the type Washington bred became valued field hands.

The opening of various parts of the frontier further increased the demand for draft animals across America. From the birth of the Santa Fe Trail in 1821 to the early days of homesteading after the Civil War, farmers, ranchers, prospectors, and stagecoach drivers took their versatile horses, oxen, and draft mules with them.

But by the 1870s, the fashions were changing. Trains replaced stagecoaches, and trolleys replaced horse-drawn vehicles in city transportation. On the farm, heavy draft horses became necessary to haul the bulky machinery of the Industrial Revolution, and were therefore imported from Europe. Cattle breeds became specialized into designated producers of either milk or beef to feed a growing population, while their draft abilities were abandoned altogether.

But even the desirable heavy horse breeds were dealt a severe blow in World War I, as they were drafted into service hauling artillery. Many casualties resulted. Mechanization eliminated the need for workhorses, draft mules, and oxen in America after the war, reducing the populations of breeds suited to these purposes.

Fortunately, many heavy horses and dual-purpose cattle breeds were preserved on family farms and ranches across the country. From these small populations, the heritage breeds were saved when the back-to-the-land movement of the 1960s and 1970s brought renewed interest in farming with animal power instead of gas and diesel. The fortunes of these draft animals waxed and waned over the next few decades, but many are experiencing revival as small farmers and homesteaders seek more sustainable methods of farming.

92. What fraction of families would typically own their own team of draft animals in a medieval European farming village?

Very few farmers could afford to keep a full draft team. The more common practice was to keep an ox or two and share with other tenant farmers, thus making up an entire team to work the landlord's fields jointly.

93. Before Columbus, did the native cultures of North and South America have draft animals or cattle?

They had no cattle, but they did have draft animals.

In North America, dogs were the preferred draft animals. Eskimos and other native tribes in those chilly northern regions had dog sleds, while the Plains Indians usually relied on a much simpler arrangement called a travois, involving two long poles dragged behind the draft dog.

In South America, packing was much safer in the mountain regions, so llamas were used as beasts of burden rather than as draft animals.

94. How many oxen pulled a covered wagon?

This would depend on the size of the wagon and how heavily it was loaded. But for an average prairie schooner on the Oregon Trail, there were probably three yoke, or six oxen.

As a side note, it is a common misconception that the covered wagon used on the Oregon Trail was a Conestoga wagon. Typically, Oregon pioneers just used whatever farm wagons they already owned or could obtain to hit the trail. The Conestoga was a heavy freight wagon used to ship goods over the Appalachians prior to railroad development. This massive vehicle could carry up to six tons of freight and might require as many as six yoke of oxen.

95. When people were going west in wagon trains in the nineteenth century, how did they get the horses and wagons over the Rocky Mountains?

The Oregon Trail route went through a convenient gap known as South Pass, where it was comparatively easy to cross the mountains.

As for individual steep slopes, several techniques were used. When ascending, teams might be doubled up to draw the wagon to the top.

Descending could be even more dangerous than ascending. Sometimes the draft animals were unhitched from the wagons altogether so that the wagons could be lowered slowly with the aid of dragging weights, such as logs. In some cases, the wagon might be secured to a tree at the top of the slope, and the rope would be let out gradually.

96. Why are oxen called Lion and Bright?

This tradition appears to prevail in England, Canada, and the United States, but is perhaps nowhere so deeply entrenched today as Nova Scotia. Why these names were chosen is a mystery, but traditional ox naming typically dictated that the near ox have a one-syllable name and the off ox have a two-syllable name. Thus, Bright is the near ox and Lion (or Lyon, as some prefer) is the off ox. Occasionally, the name Spark would be chosen instead of Bright.

Outside of Nova Scotia, traditional team names follow this same syllable pattern. Other traditional team names include Turk and Toby, and Buck and Benbow. Those familiar with Laura Ingalls Wilder's *Farmer Boy* will recall, however, that young Almanzo's team was named Star and Bright—both one-syllable names.

Science

97. Can oxen sweat?

Yes, but they don't have many sweat glands, which means they don't sweat particularly efficiently compared to other animals. This is why horses and mules are preferred for draft work in hot, humid climates.

98. How big can oxen get?

It depends on the breed. The Chianina is the largest ox breed. It can stand over 6-1/2 feet tall and weigh up to 3,500 pounds.

99. How tall is a draft horse, and how much does it weigh?

Again, it depends on the breed. Many heavy horses are 17 to 19 hands tall, and they usually weigh over 1,500 pounds. Shires may weigh over a ton.

100. Why do draft horses have feathers?

Feathering is common in many (but not all) draft horse breeds. The feathering may have protected the horse's legs from scratches from brambles. Today, draft horses are selected for feathering mostly because it is attractive.

Helpful Resources

Books

Body Condition Scoring System Benefits for Horses and Owners

http://extension.msstate.edu/sites/default/files/publications/publica
tions/P2947.pdf

Dr. Clay Cavinder

Mississippi State, MS: Mississippi State University, 2019

Handy four-page download with color photos. Includes an explanation of how to properly use body condition scoring to keep your horses in good health.

Harness Making

https://archive.org/details/harnessmaking01hasl

Paul N. Hasluck

Philadelphia: David McKay, 1904

Heavily illustrated public domain work. Covers tools, stitching, and the like, then goes on to discuss making collars, harnesses, and more.

Choosing a Breed of Cattle: 5 Needs and 40 Breeds for Selecting Cattle That Fit Your Purpose

Michelle Lindsey

Derby, KS: Homestead on the Range, 2019

Ready to take the confusion out of selecting the right cattle breed for your family? When you start by assessing the five needs of every future cattle owner, choosing between the many cattle breeds available today suddenly becomes much easier!

Draft Animal Power for Farming

https://attra.ncat.org/attra-pub/summaries/summary.php?pub=259

Tracy Mumma

Butte, MT: Appropriate Technology Transfer for Rural Areas, 2008

Free 8-page PDF examining draft animal pros and cons, along with a comparison of horses, mules, and oxen. Also includes resources for further research.

The Harness Markers' Guide

https://archive.org/details/harnessmakersgui00offi

Office of "Saddlery and Harness"

Walsall: T. Kirby & Sons, 1907

Includes many tips on making harnesses, but largely consists of specifications for harnesses of every type imaginable, including harnesses for donkeys and goats.

Videos

"Economics of Draft Animal Power"

http://www.viewpure.com/9scw6ZkVRnY?start=0&end=0

Cornell Small Farms

Excellent discussion of how affordable a draft team can actually be, along with some important tips for beginners.

"Sustainable Forestry"

http://www.viewpure.com/GAI6j6to_tw?start=0&end=0

Polyface Farm

While not about working with draft animals, this video does provide an excellent, easy-to-follow overview of woodlot management techniques for producing the high-value timber that makes logging with draft animals profitable.

Websites

Heavy Horses

https://www.heavyhorses.org.uk/

Probably one of the most comprehensive yet beginner-friendly resources on the Internet. Covers all aspects of heavy horse uses, breeds, and care.

"Cattle Breeds"

https://homesteadontherange.com/cattle-breeds/

Homestead on the Range

History, uses, temperament, health, and pros and cons of common and rare cattle breeds, many of which can be used as oxen.

"Draft Animals"

https://homesteadontherange.com/tag/draft-animals/

Homestead on the Range

The complete archive at Homestead on the Range, covering many different aspects of owning draft animals. Posts discuss the pros and cons of draft animals, various draft animal breeds, choosing the right ox yoke, and more.

"Horse & Donkey Breeds"

https://homesteadontherange.com/horse-donkey-breeds/

Homestead on the Range

History, uses, temperament, health, and pros and cons of common and rare equine breeds, including mules.

"Search For Farriers"

https://mms.professionalfarriers.com/members/directory/search_bootstrap.php?org_id=AAPF&mentoring

International Association of Professional Farriers

Find a farrier by specialty or location. Includes many farriers who work with draft horses, mules, and donkeys, as well as farriers who can correct hoof and leg problems.

Rural Heritage

https://www.ruralheritage.com/new_rh_website/index_green.shtml

An invaluable collection of resources covering all aspects of draft animals. Includes a draft dictionary, numerous articles on working with draft animals, listings of animals for sale, and much more.

The Livestock Conservancy

https://livestockconservancy.org/

An organization dedicated to preserving heritage breeds, including many of interest for draft purposes. A good way to learn more about the different breeds and to find breeders.

You Might Also Enjoy...

Choosing a Breed of Cattle: 5 Needs and 40 Breeds for Selecting Cattle That Fit Your Purpose

by Michelle Lindsey

When you start by assessing the five needs of every future cattle owner, choosing between the many breeds of cattle available today suddenly becomes much easier! This book will walk you through the process of defining your expectations and then arm you with key information on 40 common cattle breeds. Grab a pen and a piece of paper and start crafting your cattle-raising dreams today!

144 pages. ISBN-13 (paperback): 978-0997526134. ISBN-13 (eBook): 978-0997526141.

Available at Amazon.com. Find a complete list of titles at HomesteadOnTheRange.com/our-books/

Made in the USA
Las Vegas, NV
06 June 2023

73070516R00089